AKHNATON

AKHNATON

A Play in Three Acts

Agatha Christie

DODD, MEAD & COMPANY
New York, N.Y.

William Collins Sons & Co Ltd
London · Glasgow · Sydney · Auckland
Toronto · Johannesburg

First published 1973
© Agatha Christie 1973
ISBN 0 396 06822 7
Set in Monotype Bembo
Made and Printed in Great Britain by
William Collins Sons & Co Ltd Glasgow

CHARACTERS

(*In order of their appearance*)

A WOMAN
A MAN
SECOND WOMAN
SECOND MAN
OLD WOMAN
SOLDIER OF THE GUARD
MERIPTAH   High Priest of Amon
ENVOY OF THE KING OF MITANNI
HOREMHEB
HERALD
TYI   Queen to Amenhotep III
AKHNATON   Amenhotep IV
ROYAL SCRIBE
NUBIAN SERVANT
AY   A Priest
NEFERTITI   Queen to Akhnaton
NEZZEMUT   Her sister
PARA   An Ethiopian Dwarf
BEK   Chief Sculptor and Architect
PTAHMOSE   A Young Priest of Amon
TUTANKHATON   Afterwards called Tutankhamun
CAPTAIN OF SOLDIERS
PEASANT MEN and WOMEN, SOLDIERS,
GUARDS, YOUNG ARTISTS, etc.

SCENES

Note: Akhnaton reigned in Egypt from 1375 to 1358 BC

ACT ONE *Scene One*

SCENE: *The forecourt of the Palace of Amenhotep III.*

The façade of the Palace is adorned with flagstaves bearing tufts of parti-coloured pennants. The entrance to it is centre and over it is a big ceremonial balcony with columns and steps leading down one side. The whole is brilliantly painted with bright colours. There is a small entrance to the lesser apartments L.C. Main entrance from street is down right. Two soldiers are on guard in the Court.

TIME: *It is midday and the Court is full of blazing light.*

A murmur is heard off right and swells as of a crowd drawing nearer. Shouts and cries begin to be heard and a lot of excited chattering. There is a commotion outside and two or three of the CROWD *are forced into the courtyard. They are excited and chattering, craning their necks back to see.*

A WOMAN: They are coming this way –
A MAN: Who is it?
SECOND WOMAN: The foreigners. The Syrians.
FIRST WOMAN: How hideous they are!
MAN: Look at their hair . . . And their caps.
WOMAN: They *are* ugly! How disgusting foreigners are! So dirty-looking.

MAN: Oh well, it takes all sorts to make a world as they say.

SECOND MAN: What is it? What is happening?

SECOND WOMAN: [*eagerly*] They are bringing the Goddess Ishtar to cure our King of his sickness.

FIRST MAN: Ishtar of Nineveh is very powerful.

OLD WOMAN: I've heard of miracles happening.

FIRST WOMAN: Who knows, her passing may bring me luck. I may bear a son.

CROWD: [*from outside*] Ishtar, Ishtar. Ishtar of Nineveh.

SOLDIER GUARDS: Outside there, you.

> [*They clear the Court.*
> *The* HIGH PRIEST *of Amon, a tall commanding man of great dignity, appears in the centre entrance. His head is closely shaven and he wears a linen robe. With him is* HOREMHEB, *a young officer.*]

HIGH PRIEST: [*raising a hand with authority*] Peace. What is this tumult?

SOLDIER OF THE GUARD: It is the Embassy from Mitanni, Your Holiness.

HIGH PRIEST: Let them enter.

> [*An* ENVOY *enters followed by four others bearing the shrine of the goddess.*]

ENVOY: Greetings to you, my lord, and to your master, the Great King of Egypt, from Dushratta, King of Mitanni. My master, Dushratta, is sick at heart to hear of the condition of his dear brother and son-in-law the Egyptian King, Son of Ra, King and Emperor. He sends therefore the statue of Ishtar that she, the miracle-working

Goddess, may exorcise the evil spirit which causes the King's infirmity, as she has done before.

HIGH PRIEST: The Peace of Amon go with you. Enter and you shall be brought to the presence of the Great Queen, the Royal wife.

ENVOY: I thank you.

HIGH PRIEST: [to SOLDIER OF THE GUARD] Lead the noble servants of Dushratta to where food and drink is prepared for them.

[*The* EMBASSY *goes out by small door L.*]

[*to* SECOND SOLDIER] Go acquaint the Great Queen with the news of the arrival of Ishtar.

[*All exit except the* HIGH PRIEST *and* HOREMHEB, *who stands respectfully waiting for orders. He is very much a soldier and definitely a pukka sahib. He is simple and straightforward.*]

Horemheb.

HOREMHEB: Holy Father?

HIGH PRIEST: What is your opinion concerning Syrians, Horemheb?

HOREMHEB: They are marvellous riders. They ride so well they might be part of the horse. Some of them are good sportsmen, too.

HIGH PRIEST: Yes. Wild fellows, but not unlikeable.

HOREMHEB: [*condescendingly*] Of course they're absolute barbarians.

[*There is a silence. The* HIGH PRIEST *is lost in thought.*]

[*timidly*] Is it true, Holy Father, that this Ishtar of Nineveh has been sent once before to the Great King?

HIGH PRIEST: That is so, my son.

HOREMHEB: And she effected a cure?

HIGH PRIEST: [*indulgently*] The Syrian barbarians think so.

HOREMHEB: These foreign Gods and Goddesses seem a very crude lot to me.

HIGH PRIEST: We who are steeped in the wisdom of Amon know that Ishtar of Nineveh is only another manifestation of our Egyptian Goddess Hathor.

HOREMHEB: Is she? I'm afraid I'm very ignorant. There are so many things I don't know.

HIGH PRIEST: It is not necessary that you should. Egypt requires different gifts from her sons. Of her priests she requires wisdom and learning. Of her soldiers [*lays a hand on* HOREMHEB's *shoulder*] a strong right arm.

HOREMHEB: [*gloomily*] My arm is little occupied – nor likely to be! Egypt has conquered the world. Throughout the Empire there is peace.

HIGH PRIEST: And that does not suit you, my son.

HOREMHEB: One has to think of one's promotion.

HIGH PRIEST: There can only be peace where there is strength. Remember that, my son. We have a great Empire. But we can only hold it by constant vigilance. The first sign of weakness and we should have trouble from these turbulent Syrians and their like.

HOREMHEB: They're good fighters. I'll say that for them.

HIGH PRIEST: [*approvingly*] That is well, my son. A wise conqueror is he who does not despise the conquered.

HOREMHEB: A fair fight and no ill feeling. It's all the fortune of war, that's what I say. And don't kick a man when he's down.

HIGH PRIEST: [*approvingly*] Such sentiments are what have made Egypt great. Never forget that we rule these people for their own good. Without our strong hand, they would destroy themselves in a hundred petty tribal fights.

HOREMHEB: They're hopelessly uncivilized, of course. Even the Princes who've been educated in Egypt soon relapse into native customs when they get back. Do you not think, my lord, that sometimes . . . [*hesitates*]

HIGH PRIEST: Speak, my son.

HOREMHEB: Well – it just occurred to me – you don't think that all this education is a mistake? One wonders sometimes if it's much use trying to civilize them. They might be – well – happier without it?

HIGH PRIEST: [*sententiously*] It is our aim to improve all the subject people under our care. The great Empire of Amenhotep III must be one of Culture and Progress.

HOREMHEB: Yes, sir, of course. You're right. [*Pause.*] You know, I don't see why our Empire shouldn't be extended even further – *beyond* the land of the Two Rivers.

HIGH PRIEST: [*sighing*] You are young. You look forward with confidence.

HOREMHEB: Am I wrong?

HIGH PRIEST: I see the clouds gathering. The Great King Amenhotep lies near to death. When he goes to Osiris – a woman will reign.

HOREMHEB: [*respectfully*] The Great Queen.

HIGH PRIEST: Queen Tyi is a great Queen. She is the

13

Consort of the God, Divine Consort of Amon. [*Pause.*] She is the first Queen who has not been of Royal birth.

HOREMHEB: True.

HIGH PRIEST: Yuan, her father, was a wise and far-seeing noble. He had great power in the land. A less ambitious man might have been satisfied to see his daughter married to the Pharaoh, but Yuan's daughter was not only a wife. She was proclaimed Great Queen, Royal wife. She was associated with the King on public documents. That has never been done before.

HOREMHEB: [*thinks it over*] That's true. These innovations are rather dangerous . . . I don't think I like them.

HIGH PRIEST: It is easier to pull down than to build up. To break with tradition is unwise.

HOREMHEB: [*thoughtfully*] Women – you never quite know where you are with women.

HIGH PRIEST: They can do much harm.

HOREMHEB: Still, my father, the Queen will rule jointly with her son, the Prince.

HIGH PRIEST: The young Prince is sickly. He dreams dreams and sees visions. He is the beloved of Ra Harakte who is the Lord of Visions. I fear that the Prince will dream and not rule. The power will be always in the hands of his mother. It is already she who has ruled Egypt for the last six years.

HOREMHEB: When his Highness grows to man's estate –

HIGH PRIEST: [*vexedly*] I do not know – he is so strange at times in his manner. He looks at me – at ME, Meriptah, the High Priest of Amon, as though – as though I was not there. He laughs sometimes for no reason as though he saw some jest that no one else perceived. It may be that his mind is affected. [*Doubtfully.*] My son, these are very secret matters of which I speak. They must be kept behind closed lips.

HOREMHEB: Holy Father, you can trust me.

HIGH PRIEST: That I believe. You are young, and as yet unknown, but if you are faithful to Amon, you may go far. I believe in youth. [*Smiles graciously on* HOREMHEB.] Amon needs young blood, he needs soldiers as well as Priests – and it has been told me that you have the makings of a very pretty soldier.

HOREMHEB: [*flushing with pleasure*] You are too kind, my lord. Rest assured, my loyalty to the Crown and to Amon will not waver. When the Great King goes to Osiris, I will fight for His Highness the Prince with the same enthusiasm.

HIGH PRIEST: I have spoken as I have because I believe that we have troubled days ahead. When Tyi rules –

HOREMHEB: [*quickly*] The Empire will feel unrest – it will look for signs of weakness in us – but if it finds none, my father?

HIGH PRIEST: You speak as a soldier should speak.

HOREMHEB: What we have, we hold. There shall be no weakness.

[*A* HERALD *appears in centre doorway.*]

HERALD: The Great Queen, Divine Consort of Amon, Royal Wife of the Great King, greets the Messengers of the King of Mitanni.

[*The words are taken up. The* EMBASSY *procession files in L.*

HIGH PRIEST *exits through centre doorway.*

HOREMHEB *comes down stage and watches proceedings with interest. The* EMBASSY *stands waiting. Finally with all due ceremony* QUEEN TYI *appears on balcony. Richly-dressed* ATTENDANTS *are with her.* TYI *is a middle-aged woman of handsome and striking countenance. She is magnificently dressed and wears an elaborately dressed wig. Everyone prostrates themselves. The High Priest,* MERIPTAH, *stands on one side of her.* AKHNATON *stands on the other. He is a fragile-looking boy with intelligent eyes. By contrast to his mother he is simply attired. He has a bird perched on his wrist to which he pays more attention than he does to the formal scene around him.*]

QUEEN TYI: Greeting to the Envoys of Dushratta, our brother of Mitanni. Approach. My son and I bid you welcome.

ENVOY: [*prostrating himself*] Greeting to the Great Queen, Royal Wife, Divine Consort of the God Amon. Thus says Dushratta, King of Mitanni, Smiter of Lions. Let Ishtar, the Great Goddess, once again exorcise the evil spirit which causes the sickness of his brother the Great King of Egypt.

QUEEN TYI: The Great King awaits the coming of Ishtar. Let the shrine of the Goddess be brought into his presence.

HIGH PRIEST: [*raising his hand*] In the name of Amon, welcome to the wonder-working Goddess.

[*The* EMBASSY *goes slowly through the great doorway.* QUEEN *and* HIGH PRIEST *re-enter Palace.*

AKHNATON *comes down steps into Court.* HOREMHEB *watches* EMBASSY *from down stage. He is interested in the strangers. All exit except* HOREMHEB *and* AKHNATON *and* SOLDIERS *on guard.* AKHNATON *notices* HOREMHEB, *studies him and when procession has finally gone comes down stage to him.*]

AKHNATON: Who are you?

HOREMHEB: [*wheeling round and coming to attention*] Your Highness!

AKHNATON: Who *are* you?

HOREMHEB: My name is Horemheb, Highness. I came here with the High Priest of Amon.

AKHNATON: You are a priest?

HOREMHEB: No, I am a soldier.

AKHNATON: [*ironically*] Of course. If you are not a priest you *must* be a soldier.

HOREMHEB: [*interrogatively*] Highness?

AKHNATON: I have studied our latest census reports. There are only four divisions. Priests, Soldiers, Royal Serfs, and, of course, the Craftsmen. All other classes have been abolished.

HOREMHEB: Were there then other classes?

AKHNATON: You are not a student of history. [*His voice alters.*] Why should you be? You are strong. [*He touches him with a finger, running it down a shoulder muscle.*] Your body is a delight to you. But I – I am not strong. So I read and ponder over the past. I read of the time when Egypt was free, and happy, and glorious.

HOREMHEB: [*amazed*] In the dark ages? It is true, the great pyramids were built then, but look at all the inventions and the discoveries since. Even horses and chariots were unknown to us then. But now, we are advanced. Egypt leads the world in progress, in enlightenment. We have an Empire –

AKHNATON: On which the sun never sets! That is the current saying, is it not? On the whole, of all our discoveries and acquisitions, I prefer the horse.

HOREMHEB: The horse is a noble animal.

AKHNATON: It is more than noble – it is beautiful. [*His expression changes. Then ironically.*] Have you ever thought of beauty?

HOREMHEB: [*startled*] Beauty?

AKHNATON: I see you have not!

HOREMHEB: I am only a plain soldier, I know nothing about art. But I know the temples built to Amon are very beautiful.

AKHNATON: [*with intense bitterness*] To Amon!

HOREMHEB: [*with awe*] They are the wonder of the universe!

AKHNATON: Built by foreign slaves – men exiled far from their country.

HOREMHEB: [*missing the implication*] They work quite intelligently, I believe.

AKHNATON: [*looking at him*] You are dedicated to the service of Amon? You are a protégé of the High Priest. Of what family are you?

HOREMHEB: Of the monarchial house of Alabastronopolis.

AKHNATON: One of our best families! I might have guessed it!

HOREMHEB: Meriptah, the High Priest of Amon, has been good to me. He condescends to take an interest in my career.

AKHNATON: Yes, indeed. Amon knows how to reward them that serve him! A soldier could have no better allegiance. Did not a certain noble in the days gone by stand in the temple on the feast day of the God when the priests bore the image of Amon aloft amongst the shouts of the populace? The God stopped before the young noble, raised him up and had him brought to the station of the King in the temple, indicating thereby that he chose him as Pharaoh.

HOREMHEB: [*reverently*] That was the great Tutmose III.

AKHNATON: Yes. So you see, it is wise to serve Amon. Who knows where *you* may end?

HOREMHEB: I am a soldier – not a priest.

AKHNATON: [*musingly*] Four divisions of people. Priests, soldiers, royal serfs – and quite as an afterthought, the craftsmen. But above all – *priests*! Do you know that of the people buried at Abydos last year, a quarter of them, a *quarter* of them, mark, were priests. Very soon all Egypt will be priests. Then there will be nobody left to buy indulgences and heart scarabs from them – and the temple revenues will fall.

HOREMHEB: You could not have only priests. There must always be serfs.

AKHNATON: True. The land must be tilled – and the vines

planted and the honey taken, and the cattle brought out
to graze . . . [*His face lights up.*] Are you a poet?

HOREMHEB: Oh, no, your Highness.

AKHNATON: I would like to make things in words –
beautiful words. Here is a poem I have made to Ra
Harakte, the Sun God.

> All cattle rest upon the herbage
> All trees and plants flourish
> The birds flutter in the marshes
> Their wings uplifted in adoration to thee
> All the sheep dance upon their feet
> All winged things fly
> They live when Thou hast shone upon them . . .

[*Lifts his head to the sun.*] How beautiful the sun is, Horemheb. It gives life . . . [*Sharply*] But I forget. You prefer
destruction!

HOREMHEB: My lord! Your Highness! I smite only the
enemies of Egypt.

AKHNATON: [*ironically*] This is the song, is it not, that was
made to Tutmose III? [*Quotes savagely*]

> I have come giving thee to smite those who are in
>   the marshes
> The lands of Mitanni tremble under fear of thee
> I have made them see thy majesty as a crocodile
> Lord of Fear in the water unapproachable
> I have come giving thee to smite those who are in
>   the islands

Those who are in the midst of the great sea hear thy
   roarings
I have made them see thy majesty as an avenger
Rising upon the back of his slain victim
I have come giving thee to smite the Lybians
The Isles of the Utenty belong to the might of thy
   prowess
I have made them see thy majesty as a fierce-eyed
   lion
Whilst thou makest them corpses in their valleys.

[*Repeats lingeringly*] Corpses in their valleys . . .

HOREMHEB: [*quite sure of his ground*] Tutmose III was a great
King, a great and mighty conqueror.

AKHNATON: [*after looking at him a minute*] I like you,
Horemheb . . . [*Pause.*] I love you. You have a true
simple heart without evil in it. You believe what you
have been brought up to believe. You are like a tree.
[*Touches his arm.*] How strong your arm is. [*Looks affectionately at* HOREMHEB.] How firm you stand. Yes, like a
tree. And I – I am blown upon by every wind of Heaven.
[*Wildly*] Who am I? What am I? [*Sees* HOREMHEB
staring.] I see, my good Horemheb, that you think I am
mad!

HOREMHEB: [*embarrassed*] No, indeed, Highness. I realize
that you have great thoughts – too difficult for me to
understand.

AKHNATON: You are too modest. If thought is not trans-
lated into action, what is the good of thought? [*Sharply*]

21

Has the High Priest of Amon spoken to you of me? What did he say?

HOREMHEB: He said, Highness, that you were beloved of Ra Harakte.

AKHNATON: [*musingly*] A dreamer . . . Yes, that is true. I dream of the past . . . Sometimes I dream of the future . . . but the past is safer. Before the days of the Hyksos, Horemheb, Egypt was very different. There were people then who – *lived*!

HOREMHEB: [*puzzled*] Lived?

AKHNATON: That is what I said. They had houses and gardens, and they walked and talked and exchanged thoughts with each other.

HOREMHEB: [*scornfully*] An idle life.

AKHNATON: They were not afraid of being idle. Leisure did not fill them with dismay. They had thoughts in their heads and took trouble to express them.

HOREMHEB: But Highness, one cannot eternally be thinking and talking. There must be action.

AKHNATON: [*suddenly withdrawn from him*] How true! One must kill foreigners. Or fashion scarabs in the temples to place on the breasts of the dead to deceive Osiris. The sale of them increases the temple revenues and is highly pleasing to Amon. [*With bitterness*] Amon. Amon. Amon –

[HOREMHEB *looks at him in surprise.*]

HOREMHEB: Amon is good to the poor.

AKHNATON: Yes, yes, it is one of his titles, 'Vizier of the Poor who does not accept the bribes of the guilty'.

An amusing idea – and the poor believe it! Ha, ha, ha!

HOREMHEB: [*gravely*] My lord, I do not understand you.

AKHNATON: [*coming up to him*] It is true – you look puzzled.

HOREMHEB: You speak as though – as though –

AKHNATON: Go on.

HOREMHEB: No.

AKHNATON: You are wise, perhaps. It is always wise to be silent – till the moment comes. I have said too much to you.

HOREMHEB: No, no.

AKHNATON: Yes, for you belong to the service of Amon.

HOREMHEB: No, I serve Egypt.

AKHNATON: My father is Egypt.

HOREMHEB: Yes, Highness.

AKHNATON: And, soon, perhaps I shall be Egypt!

HOREMHEB: Yes, Highness.

AKHNATON: Will you serve me then, Horemheb?

HOREMHEB: I will serve you.

AKHNATON: Will you be true?

HOREMHEB: I swear it. [*With deep emotion*] I will lay down my life for you, Highness.

AKHNATON: But that is not what I want. It is not my will that my servants should die for me. I would prefer them to live!

HOREMHEB: Grant that it may be so. But a man must always be prepared to die.

AKHNATON: For what?

HOREMHEB: For his country – for his King – for the Gods –

AKHNATON: [*frenziedly*] Death, death – always death . . . I do not want men to die for me!

HOREMHEB: Yet, if need arises, they will be ready to do so.

AKHNATON: What need?

HOREMHEB: The need of your great inheritance, Highness.

AKHNATON: [*ironically*] The Empire?

HOREMHEB: Yes.

AKHNATON: Tutmose III, Tutmose IV, Amenhotep III. Those are your heroes. What were they all?

HOREMHEB: [*reverently*] They were great conquerors.

AKHNATON: [*frenziedly*] Conquerors, conquerors, do you know what that word means to me? [*Slowly, as though seeing a vision*] I hear the groaning of dying men. I see a heap of festering corpses. I see women who weep and wail for their dead husbands – and children who are fatherless. And the groans of the dying and the stink of festering corpses, and the curses of women and the sobs of children ascend to Heaven, ascend to Ra saying, 'Why – why are these things done?' And the answer that comes – listen, Horemheb – listen – the answer is very simple. It is in order that a King may set up a stela and engrave on it a list of his conquests!

HOREMHEB: [*quietly and gravely*] But Highness, we rule a conquered country wisely and well. We do not oppress the people or keep them in subjection to us. It is really better for them that way.

AKHNATON: What a comfortable belief!

HOREMHEB: These people are not fit to rule themselves.

AKHNATON: I see that you will have a most successful career!

HOREMHEB: [*simply*] You do not understand war, Highness. I have never killed a man in anger.

AKHNATON: No – only in the service of your country. That is what is so terrible.

HOREMHEB: But one does not think of it that way. It is war.

AKHNATON: It is related of Amenhotep II that when he returned as a conqueror from Syria and approached Thebes, he had with him the seven Kings of Takshi whom he had hung head downwards on the prow of the Royal barge. He personally sacrificed them in the presence of Amon, hanging six on the walls of the city, reserving the body of the seventh King which he sent to Nubia and hung up on the walls of Napatha as a hint. What do you think of that?

HOREMHEB: It probably had a salutary effect.

AKHNATON: The thought of that senseless cruelty does not fill you with horror?

HOREMHEB: You do not understand the necessities of war.

AKHNATON: It is *you* I do not understand! Your glance is kind. You are simple and unassuming. There is no cruelty in you. And yet – [*broodingly*] – I am afraid of you.

HOREMHEB: Afraid of me? My lord!

AKHNATON: We are so far from each other – you and I.

HOREMHEB: You are a great Prince and I am only one of a thousand soldiers.

AKHNATON: That was not my meaning. We speak a different language, you and I. And yet – and yet – there is a bond between us.

HOREMHEB: You are too gracious, Highness.

AKHNATON: Between your strength – and my weakness –

between your simple direct mind – and my conflicting visions. To *accept*, as you do – I wish I could. [*Pause.*] You shall be my friend, Horemheb.

HOREMHEB: My lord, I am yours utterly.

AKHNATON: When I come to my Kingdom, you shall help me rule.

HOREMHEB: [*with enthusiasm*] I will make you the greatest King that ever lived.

AKHNATON: And what can I be that is greater than those who have gone before me?

HOREMHEB: A wider Empire still – an Empire that stretches beyond the land of the Two Rivers.

AKHNATON: More lands, more subject peoples, bigger palaces, still greater temples to Amon, thousands of beautiful women where my father had hundreds? No, Horemheb, listen to my dream. A kingdom where men dwell in peace and brotherhood, foreign countries given back to rule themselves, fewer priests, fewer sacrifices. Instead of many women – *one* woman. A woman so beautiful that after thousands of years men shall still speak of her beauty . . . [*A pause. Very softly*] That is my dream . . .

> [*There is a commotion heard, voices raised in lamentation. The* HIGH PRIEST *of Amon appears in centre doorway.*]

HIGH PRIEST: Highness!

AKHNATON: My lord.

HIGH PRIEST: [*impressively*] The Great King, Son of Ra, Beloved of Amon, has gone to Osiris.

AKHNATON: [*dazed*] My father is dead?

> [*He moves slowly, as in a vision, towards the* HIGH
> PRIEST. *Before he gets there, he stops and slowly turns,
> raising his head. The sun shines down on him. He
> slowly raises his hands above his head as though seeking
> the rays of the sun.*]

Who is my father? My father is Ra. Thou art my father,
whom we call the Aton. O Sun, when thou risest in the
horizon the darkness is banished. When thou sendest
forth thy rays The Lands awake. Though thou art afar,
thy rays are on earth, though thou art high, thy footprints
are the day. Thy dawning is beautiful in the Horizon of
Heaven. O living Aton, Beginning of Life . . .

CURTAIN

ACT ONE *Scene Two*

SCENE: *A room in the Palace. Three years later. The room is hung with woven tapestry of bright colours. There is an entrance R.*

TYI *and* AKHNATON *sit on gold chairs side by side. The* HIGH PRIEST *sits a little to one side. The* ROYAL SCRIBE *holds a roll of papyrus.* AKHNATON *looks bored and inattentive.*

TYI: [*to* SCRIBE] Continue.

SCRIBE: Thus writes Dushratta of Mitanni further. 'With thy son's father I was on friendly terms. Let thy son now make our friendship ten times closer. May it be well with him, with his house, his chariots, his horses, his chief men, his land and all his possessions – may it be well indeed. His father sent me much gold, let this my brother send me more gold still. For in my brother's land of Egypt gold is as common as dust . . .'

TYI: [*to the* HIGH PRIEST] What say you, my lord?

HIGH PRIEST: The King of Mitanni writes us in friendship. A friendly answer should be sent.

TYI: And gold?

HIGH PRIEST: Ten talents of gold.

TYI: [*to* AKHNATON] What say you, my son?

AKHNATON: I have not listened.

TYI: [*to* SCRIBE] Read the letter again to the King.

AKHNATON: There is no need.

TYI: But, my son –

AKHNATON: It is not written to me.

TYI: It is written to me as Regent but it is meant for you.

AKHNATON: Consult the High Priest. Has he not control of all that goes on in Egypt?

HIGH PRIEST: I endeavour to serve you.

AKHNATON: Your disinterested nobility fills me with admiration!

HIGH PRIEST: [*coldly*] I advise that fair words should be written to Dushratta and ten talents of gold.

AKHNATON: Can the God spare all that gold? Would it not be best to give the gold to the temples of Amon?

HIGH PRIEST: This is no question of Temple money.

AKHNATON: No, what goes into the treasury of Amon does not come out again! Your holiness is the treasurer, I believe.

HIGH PRIEST: That is part of my sacred office.

TYI: [*to* AKHNATON] What would you that we reply to Dushratta?

AKHNATON: Reply as you please. I am making a poem. Would you like to hear it?

HIGH PRIEST: Let your servant hear the words of the Pharaoh.

AKHNATON: When the chicken crieth in the eggshell
     Thou givest him breath therein to preserve
       him alive
     When thou hast perfected him
     That he may pierce the egg

29

He cometh forth from the egg
To chirp with all his might
He runneth about upon his two feet
When he hath come forth therefrom . . .

[*Smiles indulgently.*]

HIGH PRIEST: [*not quite sure what to make of this*] A – a charming poem, I am sure, Your Highness.

AKHNATON: But naturally you prefer the classics. The God Amon, if I remember rightly, addressed some stirring lines to my great-great-grandfather, that mighty fighter Tutmose III. [*Declaims*]

Crete and Cyprus are in terror
Those who are in the midst of the sea hear thy roarings
I have made them see thy majesty as an avenger
Rising upon the back of his slain victims.

[*Shakes his head.*] I apologize. My chicken, hatching from his eggshell, is of no importance whatsoever.

TYI: [*with decision*] Have we any other business to discuss?

HIGH PRIEST: Nothing of pressing importance.

TYI: [*rising*] Then, my lord, we will excuse you, knowing that you have many matters of importance to transact.

[HIGH PRIEST *takes his leave. The* SCRIBE *follows him.*]

[*Angrily to* AKHNATON] Why do you behave in this foolish way?

AKHNATON: In what way, Mother? [*Conning over to himself*] To chirp – with all its might . . .

TYI: Why do you antagonize Meriptah? He has great power.

AKHNATON: He has too much power.

TYI: Hush, Amon is a great God. He has brought Egypt to greatness.

AKHNATON: And his priests to riches!

TYI: All men desire riches.

AKHNATON: Not all men.

TYI: Why must you behave like a child? To deal with these priests one must use craft – guile. Not this foolish outspoken rudeness!

AKHNATON: You do not love priests either, Mother.

TYI: I do not behave like a fool.

AKHNATON: [*thoughtfully*] No, you are a clever woman – a woman of great power. My father loved you. He made you the Royal Wife – the Great Queen. And yet you, the Great Queen, the Royal Wife, stoop to use guile with the priests.

TYI: Because they are stronger than I.

AKHNATON: You hate the tyranny of Amon. You taught me that hatred when I was a child. You dedicated me – not to Amon – but to Ra Harakte, the God of Heliopolis. And yet you use soft words – you smile – you conceal your hate!

TYI: The cunning of the serpent accomplishes more than the roaring of the lion!

AKHNATON: Lies! Always lies! I am sick of lies. I would live in truth. Truth is beautiful.

TYI: What is truth?

AKHNATON: That is an interesting question. [*Mutters*] What

31

is it? Why am I? Who am I? From whence . . . whither?
. . .

TYI: [*anxiously*] Child – child –

AKHNATON: I am no child.

TYI: You will always be a child to me.

AKHNATON: That is why you are my enemy.

TYI: [*wounded*] I – your enemy!

AKHNATON: The bird sings in the cage – but he would sing better in the free air. Between you and the priests I am bound fast.

TYI: That is not so. I seek only to guard you. O my son, my son, be guided by me – by my wisdom that has been bitter in the learning, but which has not failed me. My wisdom has brought me, a woman of the people, to be Great Queen. The priests fear me, but they dare not offend me. Leave your destiny with me – I will make you a greater king than your Father.

AKHNATON: [*as a mystic*] Only I know my Father's will concerning me. I must do as He commands.

TYI: Your Father was ever guided by me.

AKHNATON: I don't mean my Father the King, I mean my Father, Ra. Ra, the Aton, [*stretching up his hands*] whose light illumines the world, whose heat is joy, whose fire is in my secret heart.

TYI: I do not understand.

AKHNATON: [*suddenly ironical*] It is a title, is it not, of the Pharaohs of Egypt. Sons of Ra? Sons of the Sun?

TYI: Of course.

AKHNATON: But it means nothing – it is a form of words? [*Brooding*] For once, perhaps, it is no form, but very truth. Tell me again, Mother, of the days before my birth.

TYI: The children I had borne were dead. I began to grow old. There was fear in me that I should bear no son to inherit the throne of Egypt. I fancied that the priests of Amon were glad of my barrenness. Then I went to the shrine of Ra Harakte, Lord of Visions and Dreams. I swore to him that if I bore a son, that son should be dedicated to him.

AKHNATON: To Ra Harakte, Lord of Visions. And I was born . . . I . . . I . . . I . . . [*Drunk with exaltation.*]

TYI: [*frightened*] My son – my son.

AKHNATON: [*suddenly controlled*] It is nothing. Leave me, Mother. Let Ay, the priest, be sent to me.

TYI: Ay? You are always sending for Ay. What do you want with him?

AKHNATON: He is a man very learned in theology. He instructs me in the history of the Gods of Egypt.

TYI: That is well. Stick to your studies of the past.

AKHNATON: [*ironically*] And leave present rule to you, Mother?

TYI: It is on your behalf I rule. All that I do is done for you.

AKHNATON: A convenient belief!

TYI: What is in your mind?

AKHNATON: You have ruled so long, you have schemed so craftily for many years – it is in your blood now – this lust for power.

TYI: You are cruel – unjust.

AKHNATON: Send me Ay.

[*Exit* TYI.

AKHNATON *left alone, goes over his poem.*]

When the chicken crieth in the eggshell
Thou givest him breath therein to preserve him alive
[*Musingly*] Breath . . . [*He breathes.*] Sweet breath . . .

[*Enter* AY, *a middle-aged priest, a man of simplicity and learning. He prostrates himself.*]

You have come speedily – that is well.

AY: I am at your command always.

AKHNATON: You love me, Ay?

AY: I love the truth which is in you.

AKHNATON: Truth . . . Once again – truth . . . Tell me, Ay, is truth important?

AY: It is the only thing that matters.

AKHNATON: Then tell me more of the Gods of Egypt.

AY: [*expounding with pleasure*] There is great confusion there, but in the midst of confusion, truth. In the minds of the people, the simple people who till the soil, there is only sufficient capacity to appreciate the outer form of truth. With them there is only birth and death and the fecundity of the earth. There is also fear. Sekhmet, the crocodile Goddess; Hathor, the Goddess of Reproduction; Osiris, the God who speaks for the dead; Set, the destroyer – these are all Gods from the beginning of human understanding.

AKHNATON: Go on. What of the mind?

AY: There is Ptah of Memphis who speaks through the mind and the tongue of man.

AKHNATON: What of [*with difficulty*] Amon?

AY: [*scornfully*] Amon is but a trumpery little river God. As an upstart he has risen to power!

AKHNATON: Who then is the greatest God in Egypt? [*He is excited.*]

AY: *Ra. Ra Harakte of Heliopolis.* Is it not the first title of the Pharaoh – *Son of Ra*? Does not Amon, in order to maintain his title, call himself Amon *Ra*? Ra is the Ruler of the World.

AKHNATON: [*more and more excited*] And Ra is the Aton – the sun.

AY: The sun's disc is his outward expression.

AKHNATON: [*with fervour and mounting exaltation*] Yes, I have felt that – I know it. It is not the sun that must be worshipped – it is the Heat which is in the Sun – the Light that illumines the sun – it is that – that – [*excited*] that inner force – that divine fire – I feel it . . . I feel it now . . . [*Shivers. His eyes roll, he reels, then clutches at chair and sits, then quietly and in an almost businesslike manner*] There shall be no more bowing down to images carved in stone. There shall be no more exploitation of the weak – no more indulgences and amulets and heart scarabs sold by the priests to extort money from the poor. Instead there shall be freedom – and love – the love of the Aton. In one month I attain manhood. My mother will be no longer Regent. I shall rule alone. And I will no longer be called Amenhotep – meaning Amon rests. I will be called Akhnaton – Spirit of Aton. [*Rises, his hands outspread.*] I am the Son of Ra – no empty title – the very truth! [*Looks up to heaven.*]

35

Thou art in my heart
There is no other that knoweth thee
Save thy son Akhnaton . . .

[*A pause.*] Is it well, old friend?

AY: It is well. The land groans under the extortions of the haughty priests of Amon. They grind down the poor. Deliver them, my son, bring peace and rest to the humble who till the earth and bring forth food.

AKHNATON: There shall be peace for all. Happiness. Men shall dwell side by side in love – the love of my Father, Aton.

AY: It is well said.

AKHNATON: And I will build a new city. The City of the Horizon. There shall be birds, and flowering trees, and streams of water. I will live simply – not as a King. There shall be laughter there, and love, and the happy cries of children. There shall be beauty again in Egypt . . . Beauty.

AY: [*moved*] My son – my son.

AKHNATON: There shall be Truth.

[*A long pause.*]

Give orders that my Royal Barge should be prepared for a voyage and bid Horemheb come here to me.

AY: As the King commands.

[*Exit.*

AKHNATON *stands rapt in thought. The curtains part behind him and* NEFERTITI *comes slowly through. She stands for some minutes framed in the curtains.*]

AKHNATON: Someone is there. [*He smiles.*] Who is it?

NEFERTITI: It is the Royal Wife, Nefertiti. [*Strikes an attitude, laughing.*]

AKHNATON: Recite her titles.

NEFERTITI: Great King's Wife, his beloved, Mistress of the Two Lands – Living – Flourishing –

AKHNATON: [*turning*] Beloved. [*He goes to her, kneeling in front of her.*]

NEFERTITI: [*laying her hand on his forehead*] Your forehead is hot . . .

AKHNATON: I have seen visions . . .

NEFERTITI: Do not see them any longer. See me instead.

AKHNATON: When I look on you, I look on beauty. Perfect beauty . . .

NEFERTITI: My beloved.

AKHNATON: What do you see when you look at me – the King?

NEFERTITI: I see my lover . . .

AKHNATON: Ah! Your voice is like music . . .

NEFERTITI: You are tired – sit here – I will hold your head on my heart and you shall rest.

[*They sit.*]

AKHNATON: [*murmuring*] You have dove's eyes – your breasts are tender – and your hands – [*He holds them up.*] your two beautiful hands! I will fashion your hands in clay – the two beautiful hands of Nerfertiti . . .

NEFERTITI: Some day they will be wrinkled and old.

AKHNATON: Never. True beauty can never die.

NEFERTITI: You are a poet.

AKHNATON: Listen, Royal Wife. I will build a great city far from here. We will sail down the Nile and choose some fair spot. It shall be called the City of the Horizon.

NEFERTITI: That is a beautiful name . . .

AKHNATON: The city shall be beautiful . . . It shall be built by young architects working to my design. They shall not copy the old worn-out art of Egypt – stiff and symbolized. They shall draw the leaping fish, and the flying bird, and the startled buck – Yes, and they shall carve in stone Akhnaton and Nefertiti his wife – with their lips joined so – in love. [*Kisses her.*] They shall carve our children standing beside us.

NEFERTITI: Our little daughter sleeps. In her sleep she turned and murmured her father's name.

AKHNATON: Our children shall grow up in that city, our daughters – and our sons.

NEFERTITI: [*her serenity troubled*] God grant I may soon bear you a son.

AKHNATON: He shall be called Fulfilment of Aton's will. [*His lips move.*]

NEFERTITI: What are you saying?

AKHNATON: I am making a poem.

NEFERTITI: [*pleased*] To me?

AKHNATON: No, to my Father the Aton. It is a hymn that shall be sung in the Temple of the Aton in the City of the Horizon. Part of it shall go like this. [*chants*] Thou art he who createst the man-child in woman Who makest seed in Man Who giveth life to the son in the body of the mother Who soothest him that he may not weep . . . Do you like that, Nefertiti?

NEFERTITI: Yes.

AKHNATON: [*chants*]

Thou makest the beauty of form through thyself alone
Cities, towns and settlements
On highway or on river
All eyes see thee before them
For thou art Lord of the day over the earth.

[*Springs up, his hands lifted.*]

Thou art in my heart
There is no other that knoweth thee
Save thy Son Akhnaton.

[NEFERTITI *gets up, she moves a little backward, she flinches.*
Turning and seeing her.]

What is it?

NEFERTITI: Sometimes – you frighten me. You forget that I am here.

AKHNATON: Forget you? Never.

NEFERTITI: Your poems are always for God. Make one for me.

AKHNATON: I will not make you a poem, but I will build you a Palace.

NEFERTITI: In the City of the Horizon?

AKHNATON: Yes.

[*Enter* HOREMHEB.]

HOREMHEB: The barge is ready, O Pharaoh, as you commanded.

39

AKHNATON: Then let all be made ready. Let my parti-coloured tent be taken, all manner of provisions, singers and dancers. Also let my architect Bek be summoned.

HOREMHEB: It shall be done. And I, my lord, shall I accompany you?

AKHNATON: Can I go anywhere without my faithful Horemheb?

HOREMHEB: Let me be ever at your Majesty's right hand.

[AKHNATON *is amused by* HOREMHEB'*s correct manner.*]

AKHNATON: I believe, Horemheb, that you are hoping for enemies to slay. Come, confess.

HOREMHEB: Of course not.

AKHNATON: [*affectionately*] I did not mean to vex you. In a month when I am King you shall be in command of my armies. Come, let us walk in the gardens. Farewell, O Queen.

NEFERTITI: Farewell, O King.

[*Exit* HOREMHEB *and* AKHNATON.
NEFERTITI *remains lost in thought.* QUEEN TYI *enters suddenly.*]

TYI: Where is the King?

NEFERTITI: He has gone to walk in the gardens with Horemheb.

TYI: [*relieved*] Horemheb is faithful. He comes of a loyal house.

NEFERTITI: Is something wrong?

TYI: I am afraid . . .

NEFERTITI: Why?

TYI: I see danger to my son.

NEFERTITI: Danger to the King? Where?

TYI: In his own heart.

NEFERTITI: I do not understand you.

TYI: What is a King?

NEFERTITI: One who rules – one who has the supreme power.

TYI: No.

NEFERTITI: Is not the Pharaoh over all?

TYI: In name – in name. Oh, I have seen this coming for a long time. In my youth the clouds gathered.

NEFERTITI: [*bewildered*] What clouds?

TYI: The clouds of an overbearing priesthood! Everywhere temples have been built to Amon. His priests have waxed rich and powerful. Who collects taxes? The priests. For every victory over his enemies the King gained, great gifts and sacrifices were made to Amon. Today in the land of Egypt, it is Amon and his priests who have the real power.

NEFERTITI: [*timidly*] But surely – that should not be.

TYI: Child, child, how innocently you speak! Injustice should not be, the oppression of the serfs should not be – the crying of children and animals should not be – it is easily said – but these things are so.

NEFERTITI: [*confidently*] The King will sweep away all injustice.

TYI: Daughter-in-law, you are a child, even as the King is still a child. You do not know reality. In Palaces one hears only the phrases one likes to hear! But I, Tyi, Great

41

Queen of Amenhotep III, have not always lived in
Palaces. I know men – I know the bitterness of truth . . .
I know that behind the courteous word, the flattering
phrases, there lies the cunning of the serpent and the
ferocity of the tiger! Gain – gain – all is for gain. [*Pause.*]
I know well what my son has in his heart – Ra forgive
me – I helped to put it there. He has it in mind to destroy
the power of the priesthood. Is it not so?

NEFERTITI: He would have men happy – and free.

TYI: In his heart he hates Amon. There is the same hate
in my heart, but I go more cunningly to work. Open
defiance is dangerous – one must work secretly, underground, loosening a stone here, a brick there, till the
strong edifice totters.

NEFERTITI: What would you have him do?

TYI: Dissemble. Speak the priests fair. Hide what is in his
heart.

NEFERTITI: He will not do that. Akhnaton loves truth.

TYI: Akhnaton?

NEFERTITI: It is to be his name henceforth. He has said so.

TYI: Unwise – it will alarm the priests.

NEFERTITI: And he will build a city – a great city – the
City of the Horizon to be the city of Aton, the city of Ra.

TYI: Let him build a city. So do all great Kings. Let him
build in it a temple to Ra Harakte – that the priests cannot
disallow, but let him also build a lesser temple to Amon.

NEFERTITI: He might do that – I do not know. He makes
poems – beautiful poems to Ra under the name of the
Aton.

TYI: He is mad.

NEFERTITI: No, he has great thoughts.

TYI: [*bitterly*] It is the same thing! Who cares for beauty of thought? Not the serfs – they care only for bread and onions. The soldiers? They only think of advancement. The priests care only for wealth and power. The artists and the craftsmen care only for what they themselves are making. And know this, daughter-in-law, all that is new is always suspect.

NEFERTITI: What would you have me do?

TYI: He will not listen to my voice. My wisdom falls on deaf ears. [*Looks at* NEFERTITI *appraisingly*.] But you, daughter, you have the power of beauty. When your voice speaks Akhnaton will listen.

NEFERTITI: What would you have me say?

TYI: Let him build his city – let him summon artists and sculptors – but direct his thoughts to Palaces, not temples. Speak to him of beauty, beauty in art. Lead his thoughts to pleasure.

NEFERTITI: Lead his thoughts away from God?

TYI: Lead his thoughts away from danger. For there *is* danger. Would you see your husband destroy himself?

NEFERTITI: No, no.

TYI: The way Akhnaton would tread leads to destruction. He would pit himself against the power of Amon – and Amon is stronger than he is. Amon will destroy him.

NEFERTITI: Even then – [*Stops.*]

TYI: Well? What is it you would say?

NEFERTITI: [*gropingly*] I am not clever. I cannot say properly what is in my heart.

TYI: Go on. Speak . . .

43

NEFERTITI: Akhnaton is the Son of God. He says so.

TYI: All Kings of Egypt are the Son of Ra. It is a title, it means nothing.

NEFERTITI: But I think – with Akhnaton – it is different . . I think with Akhnaton – it might be – true . . .

TYI: Do not encourage him in that idea. It is madness. It will mean death.

NEFERTITI: Even death – [*She stops.*]

TYI: What wife are you to my son? You abet him in this dangerous nonsense.

NEFERTITI: I love him.

TYI: Then save him . . .

NEFERTITI: You do not understand – it is not so simple as that. When I think of my little child, our daughter who sleeps in there, [*nods*] I understand you. I, too, would want to protect her from anything. But with the King it is different – he is greater than I . . . He must do his will – and I must follow . . .

TYI: You are mad – a fool – Akhnaton has bewitched you with his craze for religion.

NEFERTITI: It is not that.

TYI: [*rising in anger and dominating the scene*] I tell you, girl, the danger is very real. I know the temper of the common people of this land of ours. In the end they will turn back to what they know, the service of the Gods – comfortable Gods of hewed stone, they will not follow into strange ways of worship. The priesthood of Amon Ra rests on solid ground. Kings have been made and unmade by the priesthood. Is our dynasty, the greatest dynasty known in the history of the Two Lands – the dynasty that has won an Empire – to perish and go down to dust? All for the madness that mounts in the mind of a man when he is young? You and I, daughter, are women. We have the wisdom of women – all men are children – nothing but children – they must be guided – coaxed with soft words and kisses. So shall we save them from the consequences of their folly.

NEFERTITI: Akhnaton is not a child.

TYI: Men are children all their lives. I know that.

NEFERTITI: Perhaps – because we choose to make them so.

TYI: You are a fool – a beautiful fool – you understand nothing.

> [*Exit angrily*.
> *After a minute* NEZZEMUT *peers cautiously through the curtains centre*.]

NEZZEMUT: Are you alone, sister? [*Enters*.] I thought I heard the old Queen's voice.

NEFERTITI: [*absently*] She has but now gone out.

NEZZEMUT: I am always afraid of her. Everyone says she is a very clever woman. She ruled the kingdom for years. She could twist the old King round her finger – everyone knows that. I suppose she was once good-looking. She is hideous now. How terrible to think one has got to grow old and ugly. [*Strokes her face. Calling*] Para – Reneheh –

> [*The black dwarf* PARA *appears*.]

Fetch my mirror. [*Noticing that* NEFERTITI *turns her eyes away*] You hate my dwarfs – why?

45

NEFERTITI: They are so ugly.

NEZZEMUT: Para is very wise. She knows the sorcery of the land of Punt. And she can make charms and love philtres, and she has the juice of a plant that gives quick death and which can never be detected.

[PARA *brings the mirror and goes.*]

[*Examining her face*] Still, perhaps you are wise not to look at her just now. It would not do if the next King of Egypt were crooked. How plain I am looking . . . Of course you were always the beauty of the family, Nefertiti. But I have the brains. And then I'm ambitious. Really, *I* ought to have been Queen of Egypt – do you remember when Para did her sand divining and foretold that I should marry the King of Egypt and be the Great Queen. I really believed her and then after all – *you* were chosen! I was very angry with Para – and she moaned and crawled and swore that the sands never lied. Perhaps the King would like me as a second wife? He's got such odd ideas about women, though, quite unlike the old King. What's the matter with you, Nefertiti, why don't you answer?

NEFERTITI: [*troubled*] I am thinking.

NEZZEMUT: Being Queen of Egypt is quite wasted on you. I'd have done it so much better. The King is so dreamy and moody – he needs someone to wake him up – to – to *run* him!

NEFERTITI: Hush, sister.

NEZZEMUT: Darling, I know I'm always frightfully indiscreet in the things I say. It's part of my character.

That's why Akhnaton and I would never have got on. I don't believe he's got any sense of humour. He's so frightfully religious, too. Religion always bored me – all those stone things with animal heads – I mean one can't really take them seriously, can one, like the common people do? It's nice for them, of course, to have something to believe in. [*Pause.*] Nefertiti, I don't believe you're listening to a single word I'm saying.

NEFERTITI: I am sorry, sister.

NEZZEMUT: You're really very sweet, darling. I don't wonder Akhnaton is so crazy about you and won't have a lot of other women. Oh well, he wouldn't have done for me. [*Pause.*] That's a frightfully handsome Captain of the Guard you have – what's his name, Horemheb?

NEFERTITI: Yes.

NEZZEMUT: Now he's what I call a *man*. I spoke to him once. He was very respectful, of course, and all that, but he didn't seem interested, even. He's simply devoted to the King, isn't he?

NEFERTITI: Yes, he is the King's most devoted servant.

NEZZEMUT: And the King is very fond of him. Men are very boring when they're fond of each other, I think. They always talk about hunting – or battles. They don't talk amusingly about people as we do.

NEFERTITI: [*rising*] I must go to my baby.

NEZZEMUT: [*as* NEFERTITI *exits*] I don't know what's the matter with you today. You're frightfully dull.

[*Enter* PARA *as* NEZZEMUT *yawns.*]

Do some sand divining for me.

47

[PARA *fetches two irregular shaped bottles of sand, gives them to* NEZZEMUT *who pours out the sand on the floor.* PARA *squats over it, rocking to and fro on her heels and uttering mechanical grunts till she appears to go into a kind of trance.*]

PARA: I see – I see – here the sand rises – but first it is low – many days must pass – many days – greatness coming – coming – I see the double serpent – I see the crown of Egypt – on your head and on his head – Lord of the Two Lands – of Upper and Lower Egypt – Ruins – Ruins of stone – workmen cutting away a name from the stone – He comes – his foot is heavy on the hills – tramp – tramp – thousands of feet – the feet of soldiers – I see the temple – I see the sacred bulls – I see – I see –

[*Her voice dies away. She shakes herself and sits up.*]

NEZZEMUT: What an old fraud you are, Para.

PARA: I am no fraud, Mistress. What I say – happens.

NEZZEMUT: That's just it – it doesn't. You're always promising me a husband and I haven't got one yet.

PARA: Two husbands you will have – two!

NEZZEMUT: I expect they'll be a disappointment when I get them.

[HOREMHEB *enters R.*]

HOREMHEB: [*saluting*] Royal Lady.

NEZZEMUT: [*looking at him favourably*] What is it, Horemheb?

HOREMHEB: The command of the King. To the Great Queen

the Royal Wife – the King's barge is being prepared and the barges of the Household. The King will journey down the river with the Queen and seek for a site for the New City.

NEZZEMUT: I will tell my sister. [*As he turns to go*] Stay a moment, Horemheb. Tell me something about Syria and your campaigns there. It must have been most interesting.

HOREMHEB: Your pardon, Royal Lady, the King's business awaits me. I must supervise the loading of the barges.

[*Exit.*]

NEZZEMUT: [*disappointed*] Brute.

[PARA *is plucking at her robe.*]

PARA: Lady – Lady – [*She points to the door where* HOREM-HEB *has gone out.*]

NEZZEMUT: [*rather as one might speak to a dog*] What is it?

PARA: On his head – on his head – [*She makes a gesture descriptive of the serpent and the crown.*]

NEZZEMUT: [*staring*] On *his* head . . .

PARA: [*nodding*] Yes, yes . . .

NEZZEMUT: On *his* head . . .

[NEZZEMUT *stares at the door where* HOREMHEB *has gone out. An entirely new train of ideas shows in her face. It becomes shrewd and calculating.*]

CURTAIN

ACT ONE *Scene Three*

SCENE: *The Royal Barge. At back is the Nile.*

TIME: *A month later.*

AKHNATON *stands in commanding position in centre of barge.* NEFERTITI *is a little below him.* HOREMHEB *is in the bows.* BEK, *a young architect, stands with plans and plumbline near the King.* A SCRIBE *is waiting to inscribe the* KING'S *words. There are* BOATMEN, *etc.*

AKHNATON: This is a fair spot. Three hundred miles below the City of No Amon. Yes, it is here the city shall be built. What say you, Bek?

BEK: The King's Majesty is unquestionably right. Here is an ideal spot for a city – a fair city such as has never been known before.

AKHNATON: Here, on the edge of the river, where the land is green as an emerald, here shall be the gardens of my Palace and of the Palace of the Queen.

[BEK *notes it.*]

Behind shall be the Palaces themselves. Trees shall be brought and planted. Behind the Palaces there shall rise the great temple I will build to my Father Aton. Further still, in the face of the cliffs, shall be cut out my tomb and the tombs of my nobles and followers. A great lake shall be made – the lake of the Queen Nefertiti. [*To* NEFERTITI] Is it well, my Queen?

NEFERTITI: It is well.

AKHNATON: Shall we be happy here, in the City of the Horizon?

NEFERTITI: There will be no happiness like our happiness.

AKHNATON: That I believe.

[*They look at each other with love.*]

[*in a loud official voice*] The King, Son of Ra, Golden Hawk, Wearer of Diadems in the Southern Heliopolis, King of Upper and Lower Egypt, the Only One of Ra, Son of the Sun, Lord of Heaven, High Priest of Ra Harakte, rejoicing in the Horizon which is His name, Fire which is in Aton – [*He pauses. All have fallen prostrate except the* QUEEN.] Ye behold the City of the Horizon of Aton which the Aton has desired me to make for Him as a monument in the great name of my Majesty for ever. For it was the Aton, my Father, that brought me to this city of the horizon. No noble directed me to it, no man in the land led me to it, saying: 'It is fitting for His Majesty that he make a city in this place.' Nay, it was the Aton, my Father that directed me to make it for Him. [*Raises his hand.*] As my Father, Ra Harakte Aton liveth, the great and living Aton, ordaining life, vigorous in life, who formeth Himself with His own hands, who is established in rising and setting each day without ceasing. Whether He is in Heaven or in earth, every eye seeth Him while He fills the land with His beams and makes every face to live. With seeing whom may my eyes be satisfied daily, when He rises in this Temple of Aton in the City of the Horizon, and fills it with His own self by his beams,

beauteous in love, and lays them upon me in life and length of days for ever and ever. I will make a Temple of Aton for the Aton, my Father, in this place. I will make for myself the Palace of the Pharaoh, and I will make the Palace of the Queen in this place. There shall be made for me a Sepulchre in the Eastern Hills, my burial shall be made therein, and the burial of the Great Wife, of the Queen Nefertiti, shall be made therein, and the burial of the King's daughter, Meryaton, shall be made therein. If I die in any towns of the north, south, west or east, I will be brought here and my burial shall be made in the City of the Horizon. If the Great Queen Nefertiti, who lives, shall die in any town of the north, south, west or east she shall be brought here and buried in the City of the Horizon. And the High Priests and the Divine Fathers and the Priests of the Aton shall be buried in the Eastern hills. The area within these four boundary stones from the eastern hills to the western hills is the City of Horizon in its proper self. It belongs to my Father Ra Harakte Aton, mountains, deserts, meadows, islands, high ground, low ground, land, water, villages, embankments, men, beasts and all things which my Father the Aton shall bring into existence for ever and ever. This is my oath of truth which it is my desire to pronounce eternally and for ever.
[*Rising into fervour and raising his hands to Heaven*]

> O living Aton
> Thou hast made thy son Akhnaton
> Wise in thy designs
> And in thy might

The World is in thy hand
Even as thou hast made them
When thou hast risen they live
When thou settest they die
For thou art duration
Beyond mere limbs
By thee man liveth
And their eyes look upon thy Beauty
Until thou settest.
All labour is set aside
When thou settest in the west
When thou risest they are made to grow
Since thou didst establish the earth
Thou hast raised them up for thy son
Who came forth from thy limbs
The King, living in Truth.

[*With wild exultation.*]

Akhnaton whose life is long
And the great Royal Wife, his beloved
Mistress of the Two Lands
[*Takes her hand in his*] Nefertiti
Living and flourishing for ever and ever!

CURTAIN

ACT TWO *Scene One*

SCENE: *The Bank of the Nile near Thebes.*

TIME: *Eight years later.*

Three women are washing clothes in the river. The HIGH PRIEST, MERIPTAH, *sits against a palm tree wrapped in a cloak – his shaven head covered and hidden by a burnous. He is apparently asleep.*

FIRST WOMAN: Any news?

SECOND WOMAN: The price of flour's gone up.

FIRST WOMAN: Again?

SECOND WOMAN: Yes, and my old man's belly takes a bit of filling up – sixteen flaps at midday.

OLD WOMAN: Everything's changed nowadays – not like it used to be in the good old days. You can't even buy a scarab to put on your dead.

FIRST WOMAN: Have you heard the latest about the new city?

SECOND WOMAN: No.

FIRST WOMAN: There's been a great carving done of the King and Queen actually kissing each other.

OLD WOMAN: No!

FIRST WOMAN: It's a fact! My son's wife's brother *saw* it.

OLD WOMAN: What's the world coming to! No decency, no religion! Look at the old Queen. *She* has dignity if you like. You wouldn't find *her* dressing herself in this thin gauzy stuff and showing herself here, there and everywhere like the new Queen does.

SECOND WOMAN: She drives with the King in his chariot on public occasions *hand in hand*.

FIRST WOMAN: No!

SECOND WOMAN: Yes. The fourth charioteer told my uncle.

OLD WOMAN: Disgusting.

FIRST WOMAN: Tell me, is it true, or is it just gossip – that the King hasn't got any other wives – only Queen Nefertiti?

SECOND WOMAN: It's absolute truth. The charioteer told my uncle so. Everyone's talking about it.

OLD WOMAN: No women at all in his harem?

SECOND WOMAN: No.

OLD WOMAN: And he a Great King! What's the world coming to!

FIRST WOMAN: Only one woman! I know what my husband would say. He'd say . . . [*Whispers to* SECOND WOMAN. *They both laugh.*]

OLD WOMAN: Be careful.

FIRST WOMAN: Oh, there's no one to hear us.

SECOND WOMAN: And the King can't be much of a man to have only one woman!

FIRST WOMAN: I'd like to see my husband having only one woman if he was a King! He'd have at least three hundred! And three hundred sons the next year!

SECOND WOMAN: Oh, we all know *your* husband is a lion and a bull!

OLD WOMAN: Talking of bulls [*lowers her voice*], the sacred bulls of Mnevis are abolished.

SECOND WOMAN: What?

OLD WOMAN: There are to be no more sacred bulls bred. [*Shakes her head.*] Evil days – evil days. No one cares about religion any more.

FIRST WOMAN: Persecuting the temples too.

SECOND WOMAN: Yes, our father Amon used to look after us. Now we haven't got a God at all.

OLD WOMAN: That's what my old man says. The sun isn't a God, he says. It's always been there.

FIRST WOMAN: And anyway you're not allowed to worship the sun. *That's* wrong too. It's the heat that's in the sun or some such nonsense of that kind.

OLD WOMAN: That doesn't make sense!

SECOND WOMAN: Of course it doesn't.

OLD WOMAN: The world's going mad.

FIRST WOMAN: Do you think it's true – [*Looks round.*]

[*The* HIGH PRIEST *snores.*]

SECOND WOMAN: What?

FIRST WOMAN: The old story about the Queen – she had no son – and that this boy was smuggled in and wasn't the old King's son at all. That his real father was a young Priest of Ra.

SECOND WOMAN: I never heard *that* story.

OLD WOMAN: It might be true.

FIRST WOMAN: They do say – [*Whispers.*]

SECOND WOMAN: Well, I heard – [*Whispers and giggles.*]

57

OLD WOMAN: Be careful. You'll get your nose cut off and your ears slit if you say these things.

FIRST WOMAN: Oh, you can do what you like nowadays! Nobody cares. If your lambs get stolen there's no one you can go to about it. They can take your hides and cheat you over your vegetables.

OLD WOMAN: It's a disgrace!

SECOND WOMAN: They say it's not so bad in Lower Egypt.

FIRST WOMAN: No, because Lord Horemheb is Governor there and he won't have it.

SECOND WOMAN: Ah! Lord Horemheb. There's a man for you.

OLD WOMAN: A proper man – like in the old days.

FIRST WOMAN: He's what a King's Vizier ought to be.

SECOND WOMAN: And he *looks* so splendid.

FIRST WOMAN: Everyone's afraid of him. No one can deceive him. He knows everything that goes on everywhere.

OLD WOMAN: That's the kind we used to have. They respected the Gods.

FIRST WOMAN: [*rising and collecting washing*] Well, that's done. It would be fun if we were ladies and gentlemen at Court. I could fancy driving in a chariot, with a muslin dress on and ribbons. [*Postures.*]

OLD WOMAN: Your husband would soon take it out of you if you tried any such goings on. He's a decent man.

SECOND WOMAN: They say it's simply frightful what goes on at Court. The dancing and the *nakedness*!

FIRST WOMAN: You don't say so.

OLD WOMAN: [*gathering up her bundle*] We live in times

of great wickedness. I don't know what will be the end
of it.

[*The* THREE WOMEN *go off L, almost colliding as they
do so with* PTAHMOSE, *who enters.* PTAHMOSE *is simply
dressed as a private individual, not as a priest. The*
HIGH PRIEST *stirs, waits a moment, then throws off
burnous revealing his shaven head.* PTAHMOSE *greets him
reverently, bowing low.*]

HIGH PRIEST: Greetings, my son, Ptahmose.

PTAHMOSE: Greetings to you, Holy Father. I thought it well
not to approach until those women had departed.

HIGH PRIEST: You showed wisdom. This is a good meeting-place, no ears to spy upon us. Moreover, the con-
versation of women, though foolish and ignorant, is
sometimes a valuable guide. Women, my dear Ptahmose,
represent very adequately what may be called the force of
public opinion. Remember that.

PTAHMOSE: I will remember it, Holy Father.

HIGH PRIEST: And now, what news from this new and
upstart City of the Horizon?

PTAHMOSE: [*producing roll of papyrus*] I bear this to you
secretly from the Royal Lady Nezzemut.

HIGH PRIEST: [*unrolling it*] And what of yourself?

PTAHMOSE: No suspicion has arisen that I am other than
what I pretend to be – a young sculptor eager to succeed
in the new art the King has founded. The Lord Bek, the
Chief of the King's Sculptors, has shown me favour and
praised my work. My position is established.

HIGH PRIEST: So far, so good.

[*He reads papyrus, then thoughtfully rolls it up again.*]

So Queen Nefertiti has borne yet another daughter?

PTAHMOSE: Yes, Holy Father.

HIGH PRIEST: [*musingly*] Clearly a sign of the anger of Amon. I think we can rely upon the people of the City of No Amon to take it that way. [*Reflects a minute.*] In the City of the Horizon is a strict watch kept for possible spies?

PTAHMOSE: [*smiling*] Oh no, my lord. I am in no danger whatsoever.

HIGH PRIEST: They consider, do they, that the power of Amon and his priests is broken?

PTAHMOSE: Absolutely.

HIGH PRIEST: How simple and foolish the young can be! The old Queen would not have been so guileless. That is why I appointed our meeting-place here, by the Nile. In the city the ears of Queen Tyi are still active. [*Studies papyrus again.*] What have you to say concerning the young noble Tutankhaton?

PTAHMOSE: Tutankhaton? He is betrothed to Ankhepaaton, the King's second daughter.

HIGH PRIEST: What of him himself?

PTAHMOSE: He is but a boy – a likeable lad of an eager and affectionate temperament.

HIGH PRIEST: Is he very devoted to Akhnaton?

PTAHMOSE: Oh yes, Holy Father. It is a cult with these young men – to worship Akhnaton.

HIGH PRIEST: Should you say Tutankhaton was of a steadfast disposition?

PTAHMOSE: [*hesitating*] Steadfast? I hardly know, Father.

HIGH PRIEST: The Royal Lady Nezzemut says that Tutankhaton is a great admirer of Horemheb.

PTAHMOSE: That is true. He is at an age for hero-worship.

HIGH PRIEST: Horemheb could always inspire youth. He has the gift of leadership. Is he still in great favour with the King?

PTAHMOSE: Greater than ever. At the King's side stand ever the Priest Ay and the Lord Horemheb. Not only is the latter Commander of all the Armies of Egypt but the King has now created him Governor of the North and all Lower Egypt.

HIGH PRIEST: Horemheb – Horemheb – the one man of outstanding ability in Egypt – a born soldier – a natural leader of men. A man bred in the faith of Amon and yet who is not with us but against us.

PTAHMOSE: Would it not be possible, Holy Father, with the offer of rich reward . . . [*Pauses significantly.*]

HIGH PRIEST: Learn to know men, Ptahmose. The man who is worth buying is most frequently not to be bought. That is so with Horemheb. To attempt such a course would be disastrous.

PTAHMOSE: It was a foolish suggestion on my part.

HIGH PRIEST: [*to himself almost*] A man indifferent to women – yet attractive to them . . . [*Looks thoughtfully at papyrus.*] As concerns the Royal Princess Nezzemut, observe all discretion, Ptahmose. Let it not be thought that there is any private communication between you.

PTAHMOSE: The utmost care is observed. As it chances, I am employed upon the cutting of a relief depicting the

61

Princess with her two dwarfs, Para and Reneheh. Opportunities for speech thus arise naturally. Other communications take place by means of Para, who is devoted to her mistress and absolutely faithful.

HIGH PRIEST: That is well.

PTAHMOSE: [*sighing*] These are evil days for Amon. Hourly they grow worse. Sometimes, in the City of the Horizon, my heart grows heavy within me. This new impious cult flourishes and spreads throughout the Land of Egypt and we are powerless.

HIGH PRIEST: You are young and impatient. You judge by the surface of things. The power of Amon is not lessened because it works secretly underground. Though the eight great temples of the God stand forsaken, though our lands and treasure are confiscated, yet the power of Amon is not broken. Amon turns all things to his own ends, the ambition and jealousy of women, the hero-worship of youth, the careless arrogance of a renegade King. Amon is not mocked, Ptahmose. The priests of Amon can work in the dark as well as in the light. Let the young fool decorate and embellish his city. The last word is not said yet.

CURTAIN

ACT TWO *Scene Two*

SCENE: *The King's Pavilion in the City of the Horizon.*

TIME: *Six months later.*

It is a light airy structure gaily decorated in colours representing bird and animal life. There are big jars of coloured faience. There is an entrance on the left. On the right there is a loggia overlooking the river. There is a long divan down R. There is a raised dais in centre. On this NEFERTITI *is posing. There are gold chairs and stools on the dais. Down L.* AKHNATON *is putting the final touches of colour to the well-known sculptured head of Nefertiti. He is simply dressed in a linen garment.*

AKHNATON: [*stepping back and looking a long time from* NEFERTITI *to the bust*] So – and so . . .

[*He strides back and adds a final touch of colour. Then shakes his head.*]

I can do no more.

NEFERTITI: [*softly*] Is it finished?

AKHNATON: [*despondently*] Yes – yes.

NEFERTITI: Can I see?

[AKHNATON *does not answer. She comes down and comes over to his side.*]

Oh! [*She draws in her breath sharply.*]

AKHNATON: [*turning away*] I can do no more. It's not what I meant. It's not what I saw.

NEFERTITI: But it's beautiful – beautiful . . .

AKHNATON: No, no, it's all wrong . . . all wrong . . . [*In a fit of artistic nerves he strides up and down.*]

NEFERTITI: [*softly*] You always say that – it is not true.

AKHNATON: You don't understand. It's not what I saw here. [*Taps his head.*] If you knew – if you only knew – it should have been – it should have been. [*He makes vain gestures trying to express himself.*] I am going to break it up . . .

NEFERTITI: [*standing between him and it*] No, no. I forbid you.

[*She is smiling a little, her tone is as to a child.*]

I will not have my beautiful head destroyed. Wait till Bek shall have seen it. Hear what he has to say.

AKHNATON: Bek – Bek. He praises everything I do. Flattery to a King – that is the only wise procedure.

NEFERTITI: Not Bek. Bek is not like that. Some of the others – yes. But Bek is honest.

AKHNATON: I tell you I hate the sight of it.

NEFERTITI: [*covering it over with cloth*] You shall not look at it again until tomorrow or even after many days. You are always like this. All artists are the same – they are always dissatisfied with what they have done as soon as they have finished it. [*Wonderingly*] It seems odd to me. If I had made something beautiful I should be so pleased. I should run about and clap my hands and call everyone and say: 'Look, look, is it not beautiful?'

[AKHNATON *smiles at her, soothed and indulgent. She speaks with sudden wistfulness.*]

But I cannot make things.

AKHNATON: [*softly*] There is no need. You are the thing itself.

NEFERTITI: What thing?

AKHNATON: Beauty . . .

NEFERTITI: [*shaking her head*] Oh no. The beauty is in your eyes – in your mind, in your heart, in your hands. There are thousands of women more beautiful than I in Egypt.

AKHNATON: To me there is only one beautiful woman – Nefertiti.

NEFERTITI: [*lifting corner of cloth and looking at bust*] Yes, I see that. [*Looking down at her hands*] It must be strange to – make things. [*Moves her hands experimentally.*]

AKHNATON: The beautiful hands of Nefertiti as she puts the Aton to rest at sunset with the jewelled sistrums. I will model them in clay – the beautiful hands of Nefertiti – [*sinks on couch*] but not now – I am too tired.

[*Closes his eyes. After a minute opens them and looks across at her.*]

What is it? Something makes you sad.

NEFERTITI: I was thinking that I cannot even make – a son. [*Speaks with deep, shamed bitterness.*]

AKHNATON: [*half rising*] My beloved.

[NEFERTITI *flies across to him and kneels beside him, weeping.*]

NEFERTITI: Five daughters – five daughters – and no son to wear the double crown.

AKHNATON: Don't – don't. Our happiness is so great – let nothing cloud it. Could we love any son more than we love our little Meryaton, our Ankhepaaton –

NEFERTITI: But I should have given you a son – a son! You know what the people in the city say – [*lowers voice*] that it is the anger of Amon.

AKHNATON: They say that here, in the City of the Horizon?

NEFERTITI: No – no. I mean in the old city – the City of No Amon.

AKHNATON: [*laughing*] Oh that, naturally the priests of Amon have to say and do all they can. Their power is broken, their treasure confiscated and given to the service of my Father Aton, naturally they run to and fro breathing out spite and evil. What can you expect from a scorpion but a sting? [*Makes a gesture.*] Let them go.

NEFERTITI: But the people – the people believe them.

AKHNATON: [*confidently*] Only the very old and stupid – those who have served Amon too long to change. Day by day the love of the Aton becomes clearer to my people. [*Dreamily*] I have given them life instead of death, freedom instead of the cords of superstition, beauty and truth instead of corruption and exploitation. The old bad days are over for them, the Light of the Aton has risen, and they can dwell in peace and harmony freed from the shadow of fear and oppression.

NEFERTITI: Do you think – really think – that they realize that?

AKHNATON: They are rather stupid, [*he smiles*] their minds

move slowly, but who on this earth would prefer slavery to freedom?

NEFERTITI: [*drawing back and frowning a little*] Horemheb does not think as you do.

AKHNATON: [*affectionately*] Horemheb always thinks the worst, bless his solemn face. Croak, croak, croak, that is Horemheb!

NEFERTITI: [*jealously*] How fond you are of that man.

AKHNATON: Why do you dislike him, Nefertiti?

NEFERTITI: [*slowly*] He – dislikes me.

AKHNATON: No, no.

NEFERTITI: Yes, he does. He despises women.

AKHNATON: He may have had good cause to do so. A soldier is not likely to see the best side of women. It is in his training to see them as booty – nothing more.

NEFERTITI: [*persistently*] Why do you care for him so? You have nothing in common. You don't share any of the same ideas. He does not even believe in your God. In his heart he is still a worshipper of Amon.

AKHNATON: No, no, Nefertiti.

NEFERTITI: It is true, I tell you.

AKHNATON: [*thoughtfully*] In a sense – perhaps. Horemheb is very loyal to ideas. He was brought up in the shadow of Amon and it will take a long time for him to throw it off. What his grandfather thought in the time of Amenhotep the Second is good enough for Horemheb. [*He speaks with deprecation but fondness.*] Strangely enough, though, I like him for it. Even to please his King and his friend, he won't pretend what he doesn't feel. There's something *real* about Horemheb. And for all his obstinacy,

67

he's not a fool. So long as it's not a matter of imagination he's very shrewd. And then he's got a magnificent body – like iron – I've always admired that.

[*A pause during which one sees by her face that* NEFERTITI *appreciates the poignancy of the pause.* AKHNATON *is keenly conscious of his physical frailty.*]

Oh, he's a good fellow through and through – real, strong, alive. One can't help liking him. Everyone does!

NEFERTITI: You've noticed that – the way the people cheer him in the streets. They say he's absolutely worshipped in Lower Egypt.

AKHNATON: Dear old Horemheb. [*Looks across at head.*] We must show him your head. I always like showing sculpture and painting to Horemheb! He looks so embarrassed and doesn't know what to say about it. Let's send for him – [*Is about to clap his hands but* NEFERTITI *stops him.*]

NEFERTITI: Wait – there is something –

[AKHNATON *looks at her, surprised. She rises and stands there nervously.*]

I must say it – I must – you must listen.

AKHNATON: [*seating himself with a grave face*] I am listening.

NEFERTITI: [*desperately*] You are the Great King – I have borne you no son. If you were to take my sister Nezzemut to wife, she also is of Royal blood – if she gave you a son –

[*She stops as* AKHNATON *rises and quells her with an imperious gesture.*]

AKHNATON: Nefertiti, you are the Royal Wife – the Great Queen. For me there is none other – just as there has not been and never shall be such a great love as is ours for each other.

NEFERTITI: [*swaying and half falling*] Ah –

[*He catches her.*]

AKHNATON: What would you have had me say?

NEFERTITI: What you did say. But Horemheb would think differently.

AKHNATON: It is Horemheb's love for me I prize, not his advice.

NEFERTITI: And your mother, she too might think differently.

AKHNATON: My mother no longer rules Egypt.

NEFERTITI: [*timidly*] But she is wise.

AKHNATON: With the wisdom of her generation. We have a new wisdom.

[*For a moment or two the mystic in him comes up. His eyes go to the sun. A movement from* NEFERTITI *recalls him. He speaks in a matter of fact tone.*]

Dear wife, be sensible. Our eldest daughter, Meryaton, is married to Smenkhara and our little Ankhepaaton is betrothed to Tutankhaton. They are both dear lads, imbued with the truth and love of God. Either will make a worthy King. So let us return to our happiness, our never-ending happiness in this, our lovely city. [*Pause.*] Come, we will send for our friends.

69

[*Claps his hands.* NUBIAN SERVANT *appears.*]

Command the presence of the chief sculptor, the Lord
Bek, and any who are with him in the studios. Also fetch
here the Lord Horemheb.

[SERVANT *prostrates himself and leaves.*]

Are you happy now, my wife with the beautiful hands?
[*He holds them up.*]

NEFERTITI: Yes, I am happy. But I am glad I said what I
did before your mother arrives today.

AKHNATON: You are afraid of my mother, like everyone
else. It is true she is a masterful woman.

NEFERTITI: She loves you very deeply.

AKHNATON: So long as I march her road.

NEFERTITI: I do not think you know how much she loves
you.

AKHNATON: She loves me as a child, not as a man.

NEFERTITI: You are unkind.

AKHNATON: Have I not built her a beautiful temple, here
in our city? The Temple of Queen Tyi. Have I not begged
her again and again to leave the City of No Amon and
come here to live? But she prefers the old ways, the old
life. She lives in the past. One should live in the future.
[*His face softens.*] Still, she is coming now.

NEFERTITI: We will make her so happy here she will never
go back to the old city.

[BEK *enters with four or five young artists including*
PTAHMOSE. *The young men are slightly decadent in*

appearance. Very fancifully dressed and inclined to strike attitudes.]

AKHNATON: See, my friends, it is finished.

[*He takes off cloth from head. They cluster round.*]

YOUNG MEN: [*in chorus*] Marvellous! Divine! Perfection! Too delicious! Too exquisite!

[AKHNATON *smiles indulgently at them but his eyes are on* BEK. BEK *looks a good deal older and graver.*]

AKHNATON: Well, my faithful Bek?

[BEK *looks long at the head, then he suddenly kneels and kisses* AKHNATON'*s hand.*]

BEK: Master.

AKHNATON: [*with a sigh of relief*] Then I have not failed after all!

NEFERTITI: [*affectionately*] I told you so.

[*Another outburst of praise from the young men. They all cluster round* AKHNATON, *who stands with his arm round* NEFERTITI. *It is all very friendly and informal.* HOREMHEB *enters with* TUTANKHATON. TUTAN-KHATON *is a good-looking lad with a rather weak face. He is always eager to win approval and is easily moved to enthusiasm.* HOREMHEB *looks rather grim at the sight of the group surrounding* AKHNATON *and clearly despises and dislikes the band of artists. For some minutes they do not notice him.*]

71

PTAHMOSE: It is by far the best thing you have done – better than the relief – though that was beautiful. You are not only the King of Egypt but the King of Sculptors!

A YOUNG MAN: A much higher title.

ANOTHER: Yes, indeed.

HOREMHEB: [*unable to help saying it*] Tchah!

AKHNATON: [*turns and sees him*] Ah, there you are, my good Horemheb – and you, my dear son-in-law.

[TUTANKHATON *flushes with pleasure.* AKHNATON *draws them both forward.*]

Come, what do you think of it?

TUTANKHATON: [*eagerly*] Oh, sir, it is the most beautiful thing – as beautiful as the Queen herself, and that is saying much.

[NEFERTITI *smiles on him and stretches out a hand. She and* AKHNATON *and* TUTANKHATON *stand together.*]

AKHNATON: And you, Horemheb, what do you say? [*There is a twinkle in his eye.*]

HOREMHEB: [*unemotionally and slightly embarrassed*] Very fine, sir. I'm sure the – er – colouring is most lifelike.

[*He tries to think of something more to say.* AKHNATON *watches him as though waiting for more. The young men keep their eyes on* AKHNATON, *ready to laugh if it is the thing to do.*]

AKHNATON: [*coming over to him*] My dearest friend.

[*He puts his arm through* HOREMHEB'*s and the latter's face softens.*]

[*Gently and with feeling*] You would admire anything that I had made because you love me.

HOREMHEB: [*embarrassed*] Indeed, sir.

AKHNATON: [*a little wistfully*] This new art that I have founded – it does not touch you in any way?

HOREMHEB: It's simply that I don't understand that sort of thing. It's my own fault.

AKHNATON: [*looking at him critically*] I shall do a head of you.

HOREMHEB: [*not relishing the prospect*] Of me? Oh, but – really –

AKHNATON: [*thinking over the difficulties*] To get the power – the strength – the play of the muscles – one should know how the human being is made under the skin. [*Ponders problem.*]

HOREMHEB: Sir, I am most anxious to speak with you. Tributaries have arrived from Mitanni and Syria, also from the South. There is the question of your speech to them to be prepared.

AKHNATON: [*impatiently*] Not now. [*Moves away a little.*]

HOREMHEB: Then there are reports that I do not like from the City of No Amon.

AKHNATON: [*sharply*] The City of No.

HOREMHEB: The City of No. The tax-gatherers –

AKHNATON: We will speak of it later. [*Turns to* BEK *and others.*] And on what are you working now?

73

YOUNG MEN: The fresco of wild geese – Reaping in the fields – Lotuses –

AKHNATON: That is good. Go out for yourselves into the fields and down by the river. Let everything be natural and true. Cut yourselves loose from the old formalities, the stereotyped ways of representing natural objects. Simplicity and truth, that is what you must aim at.

CHORUS OF YOUNG MEN: Yes, Master.

AKHNATON: And you, wise Bek?

BEK: The fresh consignments of red granite have arrived from the Upper Nile.

AKHNATON: Good.

BEK: I have progressed further with the reliefs of you and the Great Queen, but I should like you to see them before I carve them further.

AKHNATON: You have represented us naturally – as human beings – not as pompous figures of state?

BEK: Lord, can you ask me? I, your first pupil.

AKHNATON: And my greatest!

BEK: You are dancing – so – and the Queen holds out to you a bunch of lotus flowers – thus! But I would like you to see –

AKHNATON: We will come now.

NEFERTITI: Yes, indeed.

> [AKHNATON *and* NEFERTITI, BEK *and the artists go out – gay and laughing together.* HOREMHEB *looks after them. His face is desperately worried and unhappy.* TUTANKHATON *regards him anxiously. The boy has a deep hero-worship for* HOREMHEB.]

TUTANKHATON: You look full of care, Lord Horemheb.

HOREMHEB: [*seating himself*] I am.

TUTANKHATON: What worries you?

HOREMHEB: The grasp, greed and chicanery of human beings!

TUTANKHATON: I do not understand.

HOREMHEB: Unless you have constant supervision, the weak are exploited by the strong, and beneficent laws are twisted to the advantage of the unscrupulous.

TUTANKHATON: Is this really so?

HOREMHEB: Yes.

TUTANKHATON: Can nothing be done?

HOREMHEB: [*grimly*] Yes, the evil-doers can be punished.

TUTANKHATON: And then?

HOREMHEB: Then they will be careful before they repeat their offences.

TUTANKHATON: Are there many evil-doers in your province in the North?

HOREMHEB: Not now.

[TUTANKHATON *looks at him admiringly.*]

TUTANKHATON: [*hesitatingly*] You were telling me, my lord, of your early campaigns in Asis when the King's summons came.

HOREMHEB: Of course, so I was. Do you really want me to go on?

TUTANKHATON: Oh, please, my lord.

HOREMHEB: [*happy and diverted*] Well, it was like this. The enemy was *there* – [*Picks up a modelling tool and marks a spot.*]

75

TUTANKHATON: [*bending over*] Yes.

HOREMHEB: Our main forces were *here* – [*Takes another tool.*]

TUTANKHATON: Yes.

HOREMHEB: The Euphrates ran – *so* – [*Marks with chalk.*]

TUTANKHATON: I see.

HOREMHEB: They fight in close formation and their chariots are heavier than ours as they carry a shield-bearer as well as the driver and the bowman.

TUTANKHATON: Yes.

[*Enter* NEZZEMUT.]

HOREMHEB: Your Highness.

[*Stands to attention. So does* TUTANKHATON.]

NEZZEMUT: Don't stop for me. It looks most thrilling.

TUTANKHATON: Lord Horemheb is telling me about a battle.

NEZZEMUT: How fascinating. [*Sits and bends a dazzling smile on* HOREMHEB.] Go on.

HOREMHEB: [*to* TUTANKHATON] We had the advantage of mobility. Our chariots pretended to be thrown into disorder. Their bowmen fell into the trap. They dropped their bows and came on brandishing their axes and screaming and yelling. Of course, they're very wild woolly sort of fellows – very brave, but no brains.

NEZZEMUT: Yes?

[HOREMHEB *notices her very little, his main attention is on* TUTANKHATON, *but insensibly he feels more recon-*

ciled towards her as a woman who can keep quiet and listen.]

HOREMHEB: Our bowmen had orders to restrain their fire until I gave the signal.

NEZZEMUT: How clever.

HOREMHEB: Then, at a given moment, our ranks opened up, the bowmen shot their arrows. At the same time our chariots swept down *here* – [*marks place*] and the foot soldiers *here* – [*marks another place.*] The enemy was completely surrounded and we swept them into the river.

TUTANKHATON: Oh!

NEZZEMUT: How splendid!

HOREMHEB: But my word, how those fellows fought! Old Fuzzy Wuzzy can fight, I'll say that for him! Game to the last! Those fellows were *worth* fighting.

NEZZEMUT: It must have been wonderful!

[NUBIAN SERVANT *enters and bows to* NEZZEMUT.]

SERVANT: The Great Queen Tyi is alighting from the Royal Barge.

NEZZEMUT: [*in official voice*] Let her be welcomed with due ceremony and brought to the apartments prepared for her. Let notice of her arrival be taken to the Royal Studios.

[SERVANT *withdraws.*
NEZZEMUT *runs over to the loggia and looks out.*]

There she is, wig and all. My dear, how perfectly frightful she looks!

77

TUTANKHATON: [*running to join her*] Where?

NEZZEMUT: Ssh – there. Dressed just as she used to be twenty years ago! She *is* an old diehard!

TUTANKHATON: How old she looks!

NEZZEMUT: My dear, she must be about a hundred. But it's true she's aged a lot lately. Oh, look – do look, Tut, at all those old-fashioned gold ornaments. Aren't they screaming?

TUTANKHATON: Quite barbaric.

NEZZEMUT: [*throwing a coquettish glance at* HOREMHEB] We must be careful what we say before Lord Horemheb. He'll put us under arrest or something dreadful.

HOREMHEB: [*drily*] That would be exceeding my duty.

NEZZEMUT: As a matter of fact, you're a great admirer of the old Queen, aren't you, Lord Horemheb?

HOREMHEB: She is a woman one is forced to respect.

NEZZEMUT: Do you even like her old-fashioned clothes? Don't you think the things we wear nowadays are much prettier? [*Undulates her body, as she adds rather meaningly*] They give so much more freedom.

HOREMHEB: [*looking gravely at her very diaphanous garments*] That is true.

NEZZEMUT: [*turning again to window*] Of course, she *is* a character. It's as the common people say – she's every inch a Queen! And yet really she isn't even Royal by birth. But she gives you the feeling you've got to do as she says. I don't wonder the old King was wax in her hands.

> [*She has turned away from the window and come back. Suddenly to* HOREMHEB.]

It's true of you, you know, *you* look every inch a King.

[HOREMHEB *looks embarrassed*.]

[*To* TUTANKHATON] Doesn't he?

TUTANKHATON: Yes, indeed.

HOREMHEB: [*embarrassed*] Oh, I'm only a soured old general.

NEZZEMUT: Nonsense – you're terribly handsome. [*To* TUTANKHATON] Isn't he?

TUTANKHATON: Yes.

HOREMHEB: [*more embarrassed*] Really –

[NEZZEMUT *goes off into peals of laughter*.]

NEZZEMUT: I've embarrassed you. [*Comes up to him with a change of manner.*] Please forgive me. I do really admire you most frightfully – I don't mean just because you're handsome. I really mean because you're such a fine soldier. It was *thrilling* listening to you just now. I never realized before that fighting was such an art.

[NUBIAN SERVANT *runs in, in an alarmed manner*.]

SERVANT: The Queen. The Queen.

[*Without ceremony* TYI *comes in. She looks old and ill. Her eyes are for* HOREMHEB.]

TYI: I am glad to find you here, my lord. I would speak with you.

[NEZZEMUT *comes forward and greets her.* TYI *is somewhat impatient.*]

79

Leave us, my child – and you too, grandson-to-be.

[NEZZEMUT *goes unwillingly.* TUTANKHATON *obedi-ently. As they leave* TYI *sinks down on couch. She looks ill.*]

I am glad to find you here. I was afraid you might be in your province in Lower Egypt.

HOREMHEB: I left there two weeks ago. [*Keenly*] Is there trouble?

TYI: There is mischief brewing. I am sure of it.

HOREMHEB: In what way?

TYI: That is just it. I do not know.

HOREMHEB: What makes you think so?

[*He talks to her rather as he would to another man. They have no time for ceremony.*]

TYI: [*bitterly*] Should I not know that crafty old fox, Meriptah, the High Priest.

[*Sees* HOREMHEB's *expression.*]

Ah yes, I forgot, you were brought up under the shadow of Amon. You cling to the old beliefs.

HOREMHEB: It is true. I was brought up to reverence Amon. I am not a religious man, but I respect and believe in the old faiths and the old traditions.

TYI: Why? [*She is asking with genuine interest.*]

HOREMHEB: Because it gives the people what they need. Something simple and material that they can hold on to. It gives rules of conduct, help in affliction, due reverence for authority.

[TYI *nods her head.*]

TYI: Yes, you are right there. What good is this new religion of my son's to them? The principle of life represented by the sun's heat – the essential essence. What can that mean to them – nothing at all! They want the great stone statues that they can feel and touch, the voice of the priest that speaks through the God's mouth – the comforting lesser deities, each for a special need. Yes, the people need Gods, not a God. Ah, if only the priests had not abused their power.

HOREMHEB: [*cautiously*] As to that, I cannot say.

TYI: I forgot. You are the special protégé of the High Priest of Amon.

HOREMHEB: He was good to me and showed me favour. I owe much to him.

TYI: Then, perhaps, you are not the man I need – [*She looks suddenly very weary.*]

HOREMHEB: What makes you say that?

TYI: One cannot serve two masters. On the one side Amon and the old ways – on the other Akhnaton and the new.

HOREMHEB: I do not. I serve one. I serve the King.

TYI: Is that true?

HOREMHEB: The King, first, and for ever.

TYI: Even if it comes to King versus God?

HOREMHEB: I have told you, I am not a religious man. I respected the state religion – this new one seems to me a queer kind of madness – but all these things I leave to those more competent to judge.

TYI: So if you have to choose between Amon and the King –

HOREMHEB: There is no choice. I am the King's man.

TYI: You swear that to me, Horemheb, on the head of my son?

HOREMHEB: I swear it. My life is the King's – I would lay it down – [*Stops.*]

TYI: What is it?

HOREMHEB: Something he once said to me –

TYI: Yes?

HOREMHEB: That he wanted men not to die for him but to live for him.

TYI: It is a more difficult thing to do.

[*He stares at her – puzzled.*]

Listen, Horemheb, I trust you. You are the only man in Egypt I *do* trust today. The only man I can be sure of not to betray his master. You come of a loyal house.

[HOREMHEB *bows his head.*]

TYI: Besides, you are the only man near my son with the least ability. He surrounds himself with painters and dancers and sculptors – and not a scrap of brains between them!

HOREMHEB: Soft. A soft lot! [*Speaks with immense contempt.*]

TYI: Now listen, while my son lives here and dreams of peace and eternal harmony, I have been his eyes and ears in the old city. [*Smiles.*] I always had my little band of spies even in the old days. I know what goes on.

HOREMHEB: What is going on?

TYI: There is unrest. The people are discontented – restless.

HOREMHEB: Why should they be? Taxes have been re-
mitted. Heavy penalties have been replaced by mild ones.
Life has been made easier for the poor.

TYI: So it has been written down. But what is the writing
down of a law if there is no one to see that the law is
enforced?

HOREMHEB: Very true.

TYI: The tax-gatherers drive in the cattle, and take the wine
and flour and honey, and since there are none to check
them their own pockets grow fat.

HOREMHEB: Naturally – that would be so.

TYI: It is the same everywhere. Exploitation – greed – injustice.

HOREMHEB: Does no one tell the King of this?

TYI: [drily] The King has been told.

HOREMHEB: Well, then –

TYI: How would you deal with such conduct, Horemheb?

HOREMHEB: Cut off the noses and the right hands of one
hundred of the chief offenders.

TYI: [nodding] Yes. My son wrote a manifesto – extolling
the beauty of Truth and Justice – and bade these men
have changed hearts. [A pause.] What do you say?

HOREMHEB: The King has too exalted a mind. He who is
goodness cannot understand the wickedness that is in the
hearts of men.

TYI: And the priests, you understand, egg the tax-gatherers
on. They urge the cause of injustice secretly, murmuring
a word here and there. And already it goes about among

83

the people: Amon was the protector of the poor. Our father Amon defended our cause. This new God does not care.

HOREMHEB: Is that all?

TYI: No, there is something more afoot. Outwardly I have continued on good terms with Meriptah. His power is ostensibly broken, his temples and treasure taken away; he is nevertheless far from being a broken man. He has brains and courage and vision. He and I play an old game together – neither of us knowing how far the other is deceived. But there is something afoot, Horemheb – I know it.

HOREMHEB: But what in particular?

TYI: [despairing] I am growing old – old and tired. Death comes near . . . I cannot think and see as I used to do. But I imagine – [She pauses.] Tell me, does Akhnaton contemplate any new measures against the priests?

HOREMHEB: Not that I know of. Persecution is not part of his noble nature. He has broken the power of Amon and confiscated its wealth. But his subjects are free to worship as they choose, though he believes that the worship of Amon will soon fade and die out and all Egypt will worship the Aton.

TYI: I am wrong then.

HOREMHEB: What did you think?

TYI: Listen, Horemheb, I spoke fair words to Meriptah, offered to plead with my son that a certain measure of gold and possessions might be restored to Amon. It has been my policy to seem to disapprove of my son's religion. You understand?

HOREMHEB: Yes. You wanted him to show his hand.

TYI: He is too clever, I think, to be wholly deceived, but he *does* believe that I am fretted and angered by my own loss of power. He believes that I would make an alliance with him to gain more power back into my own hands.

HOREMHEB: Yes, I can see that.

TYI: So, as I say, I offered to be his intermediary, but at once he hemmed and hawed and sought – very subtly – to dissuade me. It would be of no avail, he said. Better to wait. The King, he said, was bitter against Amon and meditated new revenge.

HOREMHEB: [*with decision*] That is not so – I am sure of it.

TYI: Then all is well – for understand, Horemheb, *that must not be.*

HOREMHEB: I am not sure that I have your meaning clearly –

TYI: There must be no fresh moves against the priests of Amon. That would be playing into Meriptah's hands.

HOREMHEB: You think that?

TYI: Persecution is a double-edged weapon. There is nothing like persecution for reawakening enthusiasm. Already the people sigh for Amon and tell stories of his goodness to the poor. But at least they can still worship as they choose. If there were to be some definite edict –

HOREMHEB: I see . . . But I do not think you need fear. The King is much less obsessed by his old fanatical feeling against the priests. He is occupied with the arts and with the perfecting of the city.

TYI: That is well. But see to it, Horemheb, that the priests do not force his hand. Meriptah is clever.

HOREMHEB: You have nothing definite?

TYI: Nothing – but the look in a priestly eye.

HOREMHEB: I will be very watchful.

TYI: May Ra Harakte bless you, Horemheb, for your love and loyalty to my son.

[*He kisses her hand.*]

[*In a different tone*] Do you see much of Nezzemut?

HOREMHEB: [*surprised*] The Princess? No – why?

TYI: I wondered. I should not trust her overmuch if I were you.

HOREMHEB: I am not much in the company of women.

[AKHNATON *enters with* NEFERTITI *and* TUTAN-KHATON. *He comes to* TYI *and greets her affectionately.*]

AKHNATON: So you have come to dwell with us at last? Your palace is ready. Your Temple is completed. [*Eagerly*] Is it not fair, my city? Have you seen its lakes and its buildings and the trees – and the birds – have you noticed the birds? Some of them have been snared and brought from far away. I love the birds. They fly up in the sky and sing their song to their Father Aton and are dear to him.

TYI: It is a beautiful city.

AKHNATON: It is the city of happiness and peace.

HOREMHEB: There are other cities not so happy, sir. Urgent letters have come from Ribaddi of Byblos. The Khabiri grow bold and continually sweep down and ravish the flocks and herds. The whole coast of Syria is insufficiently garrisoned. More troops should be sent there. The hill robbers grow bold thinking there is none to punish them.

AKHNATON: [*sighing*] Why must there always be destruction? We will write a proclamation and it shall be read aloud in the cities of Syria declaring my will that these depredations shall cease.

HOREMHEB: It would be better to send a regiment.

AKHNATON: That would be only prevention. One must reach further down. [*Walking up and down.*] People *must* learn to live in peace and amity together. When they have been long oppressed and harried with wars and bloodshed the idea is foreign to them. But it will come! The example of Egypt, that great civilized land, will be followed by these lesser peoples.

[HOREMHEB *does not answer. His silence is a dissent.*]

TYI: In the cities of civilized Egypt all is not well, my son. The people of No Amon, for instance, are exploited and cheated.

AKHNATON: By the priests?

TYI: Not this time. Your appointed tax-gatherers abuse their position.

AKHNATON: That is bad. I would have my people free of burdens to live and prosper.

HOREMHEB: I would suggest, sir, that an example should be made of the principal offenders. If their noses and hands were cut off it would have a very salutary effect.

AKHNATON: You think so. [*He smiles a little.*] If a man lost his nose, Horemheb, can you make him another?

HOREMHEB: [*staring*] No, of course not.

87

AKHNATON: Can you grow a new hand of flesh and blood from a withered stump? [*Pause.*] Are you not afraid, Horemheb, to destroy so easily that which you cannot restore?

HOREMHEB: I do not understand you, sir.

TYI: I do.

AKHNATON: [*turning to her*] And what do you say, Mother?

TYI: That for the welfare of the common people it is well that there are people like Horemheb who do *not* understand your meaning.

AKHNATON: *You* say that?

TYI: I say that – being old and having seen the way of the world.

AKHNATON: There is only one true course – the love and beneficence of my Father, Aton. One must open blind eyes – not destroy the flesh and blood that my father has made.

HOREMHEB: Your heart is too gentle, sir.

AKHNATON: And your heart is a rock – a rock of strength.

[*He holds out his hand affectionately. Then with a change of manner*]

And now what is this about tribute?

HOREMHEB: The tributaries await your Majesty's pleasure.

AKHNATON: Shall we receive them now? What do you say, Mother? It will amuse you. They shall pass before us here.

TYI: You will put on your ceremonial robes first to receive them in state.

AKHNATON: Why should I? No, let them find the King of
Egypt simply dressed and living a simple life. Let them
see that I, the King, am but a man like themselves – let
them realize the great truth – all men are brothers.

TYI: Bad policy. The King should always be garmented
in awe – a man apart.

AKHNATON: A God, not a man – that is what you would
say. Yet if a God comes down to earth, he would, I
think, be simple. If a God comes down to earth . . . [*His
face grows mystic.*] I wonder . . . [*To himself*] Am I?
[*Looks up to Heaven.*]

TYI: Receive them on your throne, the double crown on
your head. I pray of you, my son, let them be awed by
the majesty of Egypt. Remember the words of the Great
King in days gone by. 'A Prince is a Prince of whom one
is afraid. Be not known to the people and they shall not
say "He is only a man." '

AKHNATON: That is not our way. Come, wife, sit here
beside me. And you, my mother, sit in that chair. Go,
Horemheb, let the tributaries enter.

[*He sits on dais with* NEFERTITI *beside him.*]

TYI: [*sharply*] This informality is absurd. With your friends
and your immediate circle it is one thing – but this is a
public matter.

HOREMHEB: I do beseech you, my lord – with all due
deference. Remember – I know these people. I have
many friends among them. Their minds are simple –
childish – they look upon Egypt with wonder and awe.
What is needed is so to dazzle them with the magnificence

89

of the great King that they will go home with no spirit in them!

AKHNATON: Awed and browbeaten by my wealth and power – a delightful picture!

HOREMHEB: My lord, it is the picture they desire to see. The Pharaoh of Egypt is a legend to them – a name – they want to see not a man, but a God!

AKHNATON: The son of Ra *is* a God.

[*A short pause.*]

HOREMHEB: What I should say is they want to see their idea of a God.

AKHNATON: If they have false ideas it is our business to disperse that false vision – not to foster it.

TYI: Dreamer – dreamer . . .

AKHNATON: There is only one thing to be worshipped – Truth. Come, bid the tributaries attend us!

[*They group themselves.* HOREMHEB *goes out.*]

TYI: My son – my son – will you have none of my love – of my wisdom – a wisdom that I have garnered through the long years for your sake only?

AKHNATON: [*gently*] Dear Mother, your wisdom is of the past.

TYI: My wisdom is of all time! It is the knowledge of the hearts of men and women.

AKHNATON: No. There is an inwardness of the heart that you cannot see or feel.

TYI: I see you risking Egypt for a dream – and I can do

nothing – nothing – [*her hand to her heart*] and my time is short – short – [*Subsides.*]

AKHNATON: [*to* TUTANKHATON] Come, dear lad. Sit here, by my feet. Where are my daughters?

NEFERTITI: They are sailing on the big lake.

AKHNATON: True, I had forgotten.

[BEK *enters with his companions.*]

Come, Bek, we may find matter to interest us here.

ARTISTS: How amusing. I expect they'll be *quite* impossible.

[*The* TRIBUTARIES *are announced and enter. They fall flat on their faces and then rise passing across with their gifts. Bars of gold, bags of gold-dust borne by befeathered Negroes, ostrich eggs and feathers from Libya. Wild animals in cages from Syria, beautiful nearly nude girls, bows, spears and shields from Syria, and horse trappings. When the pageant is over the* KING *rises and stretches out an arm. Everyone falls prostrate.* AKHNATON *speaks, almost chants, in a sweet voice.*]

AKHNATON: Oh Aton, father of all living, our merciful father. Thou didst create the earth according to thy desire. The countries of Syria and Nubia, the Land of Egypt. Thou makest a Nile in the sky for the countries of the strangers that water might fall upon those lands and ripen their crops. Thy love is for all equally – So, then, is my love . . . For the dweller in the Eastern desert, for the dweller in Nubia, for the man of Syria and the inhabitant of the Land of the Two Rivers – all they and the dwellers in the land of Egypt are equally my children. All men

91

are brothers. Let them live together in love and peace.

[*Pause.*]

[*to* HOREMHEB] Let these weapons be prized for the beauty of their workmanship but let them no more be seen in the hands of my people nor let them be turned against any man. Release the bonds of the slaves, give them food and drink and let them work to beautify this my city, toiling not overlong each day and having plenty of food and drink. Let the gold be given to the House of my Father Aton and used to make new houses in which to praise him throughout the land of Egypt. And for you, O Messengers, go back to your lands bearing my words. Peace go with you and goodwill each to the other.

[*There is a confused murmur, but the* TRIBUTARIES *are puzzled and out of their depth. They retire uncertainly.*

HOREMHEB *is frowning.* QUEEN TYI *has a hand to her heart; she looks ill. When the Strangers have gone out* AKHNATON *looks at the stern* HOREMHEB.]

Dear friend, will you not admit the truth that I have just spoken? You love the sword, I know, but will you not put it aside for my sake? There shall be no more swords drawn, and no arrows sped to stick quivering in human flesh, no spears to transfix living bodies.

HOREMHEB: Would that it might be so, my dearest lord.

AKHNATON: It shall be so.

HOREMHEB: [*shaking his head*] Some of the people in these far-off regions are little better than animals.

AKHNATON: Animals fight for food or out of fear. When there is no fear and no want, men will no longer seek to destroy.

TYI: Ah –

[*She springs up, pointing at* PTAHMOSE. *At the same time she has a kind of seizure.*]

TYI: Who is that – that?

[PTAHMOSE *quickly slips behind the group and disappears.*]

NEFERTITI: Who? What?

TYI: [*thickly as she sways on her feet*] I have seen his face before – in the Temple – danger –

[HOREMHEB *catches her as she sways and is about to fall.*]

AKHNATON: [*imperiously*] Let my physicians be fetched to minister to the Queen. [*Comes to her – with deep affection.*] Mother.

TYI: [*not looking at him but at* HOREMHEB] Remember . . . Your promise . . .

[HOREMHEB *bows his head. She is satisfied.*]

AKHNATON: [*in anguish*] Mother.

TYI: [*slowly and with difficulty, seeing a memory rather than* AKHNATON] My – little – son . . .

[*She dies.*]

CURTAIN

93

ACT TWO *Scene Three*

SCENE: *A room in the Palace. A year later. It is hung with bright hangings. There is an entrance L.*

HOREMHEB *and* TUTANKHATON *are busy with a pile of armour. The latter is polishing a spear.*

HOREMHEB: Splendid – that is how it should shine. One must go on rubbing until one can see one's face in it.

TUTANKHATON: [*holding it up*] How is that?

HOREMHEB: Good enough. You've got the makings of a first-class soldier, my boy.

TUTANKHATON: [*flushed and pleased*] Have I? Have I really? Will you take me with you on your next campaign?

HOREMHEB: Willingly.

TUTANKHATON: That's a promise.

HOREMHEB: Too easy a one. There is not likely to be a campaign.

TUTANKHATON: [*somewhat crestfallen*] No, I suppose not.

[*A pause.* HOREMHEB *sighs.*]

You are sad, my lord.

HOREMHEB: No – not exactly sad. [*Slowly*] A man is inclined to fret when he's debarred from plying his trade.

TUTANKHATON: You would like to fight.

HOREMHEB: Not for the fighting's sake. [*Hesitates.*] But to see Egypt – Egypt – treated with insolence –

94

TUTANKHATON: Where is that?

HOREMHEB: In Hanigalbat – an insolent message in lieu of the annual tribute –

TUTANKHATON: Who has done that?

HOREMHEB: Last month the King of Mitanni dared to detain the Pharaoh's envoy and sent an insolent message when we protested. The King of Babylon had the damned impertinence to write and complain that his messengers had been robbed in Egyptian territory and the Pharaoh must – *must*, mark you – make good their losses. The Hittites are moving south and they, too, are insolent in their tone.

TUTANKHATON: And we do nothing about it? We could, I suppose?

HOREMHEB: We have the power to loose an army which would silence all insult.

TUTANKHATON: The King, my father-in-law, has remonstrated with them.

HOREMHEB: Remonstrated with them? Those people don't understand soft words. Do you know what they think? They think we are afraid.

TUTANKHATON: Is that true?

HOREMHEB: Egypt – afraid of a handful of mountain swashbucklers and desert rovers? The idea's laughable – and yet not really laughable at all. It's the thin end of the wedge.

TUTANKHATON: How?

HOREMHEB: There's such a thing, you know, as prestige. Egypt stands for a definite idea. She stands for invincible strength and for justice. These little countries rob and prey upon each other incessantly. Egypt has imposed peace upon them. They are to live in amity and brotherhood by Egypt's command. Because, if they do not, the wrath of Egypt will descend upon them. But now – they ask themselves – what if Egypt is no longer a lion? What if there is no wrath to descend? Then, once more, there will be pillage and rape and incessant warfare amongst the tribes – all the good work undone and the people plunged back in barbarism.

TUTANKHATON: [*impressed*] I have never thought of these things.

HOREMHEB: [*bitterly*] Here, in this city, what is there to think of but pleasure?

TUTANKHATON: It is so beautiful here.

HOREMHEB: Beauty – beauty – what is all this madness about beauty? After all, what can beauty do for the world? It can't make the crops grow, it can't give justice to the oppressed. To my mind, a decently run province, well policed, where the people can grow their crops unafraid and get on with the business of living, is worth a dozen statues – or a Palace full of reliefs and woven hangings.

TUTANKHATON: I see what you mean – Yes, I see what you mean.

HOREMHEB: But you mustn't listen to me. It's just really that I don't appreciate Art. Poetry sends me to sleep and all this talk about feeling in art and significant form, and rhythm in statuary just goes straight over my head.

[*Enter a* NUBIAN SERVANT.]

SERVANT: My lord, two emissaries have arrived from Syria and would have speech with you. They bid me tell you that they are the sons of Ribaddi.

HOREMHEB: The sons of Ribaddi? I will come at once.

[*Exit with* SERVANT.

TUTANKHATON continues to rub his armour. Picks up a spear and goes through the motion of hurling it. As he is enjoying himself the HIGH PRIEST *enters disguised in long woollen Syrian dress, sugar-loaf hat and turned-up shoes. He watches for some moments.* TUTANKHATON *turns and is startled.*]

TUTANKHATON: Oh! I did not know anyone was there.

HIGH PRIEST: [*hurriedly*] I am of the following of the sons of Ribaddi. I was commanded to await my Lord Horemheb here.

TUTANKHATON: Oh, yes. I expect he will be back soon.

HIGH PRIEST: May a humble foreigner be permitted to ask the name of the noble Egyptian to whom he speaks?

TUTANKHATON: I am Tutankhaton, shortly to be son-in-law of the Great King.

[HIGH PRIEST *bows with reverence.*]

HIGH PRIEST: You are he, then, of whom great things are said.

TUTANKHATON: [*surprised*] I?

HIGH PRIEST: Yes, it is prophesied of you that you in turn shall sit upon the throne of Egypt and shall be a greater King than he that went before you.

A.—G

TUTANKHATON: [*embarrassed but pleased*] Oh, but I'm sure that is nonsense.

HIGH PRIEST: It is known that you have great abilities. [*Thoughtfully*] You could be a great commander of men.

TUTANKHATON: Oh, I don't think so.

HIGH PRIEST: Lord Horemheb thinks very highly of you.

TUTANKHATON: Does he? I am pleased.

HIGH PRIEST: It is said of you that you will lead Egypt to new victories.

TUTANKHATON: [*eagerly*] That *I* shall? [*Then checks suddenly.*] There is to be no more war.

HIGH PRIEST: Of course. The new religion forbids it. It was Amon Ra who led Egypt to victory.

TUTANKHATON: There is very little left now of the religion of Amon in Egypt.

HIGH PRIEST: In some ways, perhaps, that is a pity. All the great conquerors of Egypt, all those whose names will go down to history, were followers of Amon.

TUTANKHATON: [*thoughtfully*] Yes, that is so, I suppose.

HIGH PRIEST: There is no doubt that Amon rewards liberally those who serve him. Is it not said, 'How bountiful are the possessions of him who knows the gifts of that God. Wise is he who knows him. Favoured is he who serves him. There is protection for him who follows him.'

TUTANKHATON: Our Father, the Aton, surrounds us with peace and love.

HIGH PRIEST: But not with power and fame.

TUTANKHATON: No.

[HOREMHEB *enters rapidly. He looks worried.*]

HOREMHEB: My Lord Tutankhaton, come, I beg you, with me to the King – I – [*Breaks off as he sees* HIGH PRIEST.] *You*, Holy Father.

HIGH PRIEST: I myself –

HOREMHEB: [*stammering*] But how – why –

HIGH PRIEST: To beg a favour from you.

HOREMHEB: But indeed, Holy Father, I can do nothing –

TUTANKHATON: Holy Father? [*Stares.*] Who is this man?

[HOREMHEB *hesitates;* HIGH PRIEST *signs to him to speak.*]

HOREMHEB: This is the High Priest of Amon.

TUTANKHATON: The High Priest of Amon?

HIGH PRIEST: [*speaking with dignity*] Even so, my son. A High Priest, his pride brought low, comes shamefully and secretly in disguise to seek a favour from one whom he once befriended.

HOREMHEB: [*embarrassed*] Indeed, Father, I have not forgotten your goodness to me in the old days. How you singled me out and took an interest in my career. Believe me, I am not ungrateful.

HIGH PRIEST: I know, my son, that a noble heart does not forget benefits received – only a mean nature is embarrassed and seeks to forget. I did not think for a moment that you would have forgotten the old days.

HOREMHEB: [*still embarrassed*] No, that is true.

HIGH PRIEST: So I have come to you, Horemheb, in my hour of need.

HOREMHEB: Alas, Father, it is utterly distasteful to me to have to say it but I cannot do anything for you. I know

99

how you must look upon me – as a traitor to – to all the beliefs of my youth. But that's finished and done with. I've made my choice. Officially I worship the Aton.

HIGH PRIEST: Officially, perhaps, but not with conviction.

HOREMHEB: I've never been a religious sort of man.

HIGH PRIEST: No, but you have been a man of loyalty – loyal to old friends.

HOREMHEB: Sometimes – loyalties conflict.

HIGH PRIEST: That is true.

HOREMHEB: [desperately] Understand once and for all, Holy Father, and forgive me for putting it bluntly. I am the King's man. I serve the King.

HIGH PRIEST: You see it like that – between Amon and the King. And you are for the King.

HOREMHEB: Yes. That's just it.

HIGH PRIEST: That I knew already. And between Egypt and the King?

HOREMHEB: I don't understand you.

HIGH PRIEST: It is quite plain. Your loyalty is to your King and your country – but which comes first?

HOREMHEB: They are the same.

HIGH PRIEST: They have been – in the past.

HOREMHEB: What do you mean?

HIGH PRIEST: Nothing. Only a thought that I would have you consider. I, too, love Egypt. [Pause.] But you are mistaken when you assume that I came here to call upon your old allegiance to the cause of Amon. I come quite simply as an old friend in danger and distress.

HOREMHEB: Danger and distress?

HIGH PRIEST: Yes. I ask of you, for old friendship's sake, to plead with the King on my behalf.

HOREMHEB: The King oppresses no man.

HIGH PRIEST: You do not know what has happened.

HOREMHEB: What has happened?

HIGH PRIEST: There has been a rising in the City of No. The people have wrecked the new temple of the Aton and have sought to restore power to Amon.

HOREMHEB: Is this really so?

HIGH PRIEST: Yes. It was none of my contriving. [*Bitterly*] But I can hardly hope I will be believed. I come to beg you to plead with the King on my behalf that he shall not strike me down in anger or visit his anger on the luckless priests in the City of No.

HOREMHEB: Indeed, Father, I will willingly plead with the King on your behalf. But have no fear – he is gentle and always disposed to mercy.

HIGH PRIEST: My son, you have a big and noble heart – one that does not desert an old friend.

[*As he speaks* AKHNATON *parts hangings in centre and stands for a minute or two unperceived.*]

AKHNATON: [*in his ironical voice*] Dear me. Can it be that my old friend, Meriptah, has changed his nationality? [*Comes forward.*] I did not know, Holy Father, that you were one of my Syrian subjects.

HIGH PRIEST: Your Majesty. [*Makes obeisance.*]

AKHNATON: A very interesting meeting. I heard you had Syrian guests, Horemheb, but I had no idea as to their identity.

HIGH PRIEST: Your Majesty, you must believe me – Lord Horemheb knew nothing of my coming. This is no intrigue between us, as you may think. I –

AKHNATON: [*coldly*] My lord, you judge my mind by the thoughts of your own.

HOREMHEB: [*not embarrassed because he is sure of his own honesty*] It is true, sir, I had no idea of his coming.

AKHNATON: That I know. I have not doubted you, Horemheb.

HOREMHEB: You trust too much, sir.

AKHNATON: Trust *you* too much! That would be impossible.

HOREMHEB: You are safe in trusting me. [*Smiles.*] But it is advisable always to retain a little suspicion. You do not know the world as I do.

AKHNATON: I will try and learn distrust – even of you.

HOREMHEB: [*gravely*] It would be better to distrust me and others – than to trust too many.

AKHNATON: You are wrong. Trust and love, those are the two great weapons that shall remake the world anew.

HOREMHEB: There are some people, sir, who do not understand these qualities. There is grave news from Syria. The Hittites are marching south, putting all to the sword. Itakhama has proclaimed himself King of Kadesh and has cut off the loyal city of Tunip. The faithful Ribaddi, King of Byblos, who is your loyal servant, sends his son to urge you to send help quickly to relieve the garrison of Simyra. If Simyra falls, Byblos cannot hold out. He will defend it to the death but he begs that troops may come quickly. The Khabiri, the scourge of the desert, are laying waste the town and villages and burning and sacking the land.

AKHNATON: Oh, what evil is in men's hearts. [*With anguish*] When will men learn to love each other and live in peace and brotherhood?

HOREMHEB: I demand the King's permission to despatch forthwith two regiments to –

AKHNATON: No.

HOREMHEB: But, sir, these people must have justice. The name of Egypt stands for justice.

AKHNATON: In the future let it stand for mercy. Messengers shall be sent but no armed force.

HOREMHEB: You will make the name of Egypt a mockery all over the Empire!

AKHNATON: To meet violence with violence is to breed yet more violence.

HOREMHEB: Shall dead men then not be avenged?

AKHNATON: Their deaths are beautiful since they died in loyalty.

HOREMHEB: They were my friends –

AKHNATON: Could vengeance bring them back to life?

HOREMHEB: No, but –

AKHNATON: You must learn to forgive.

HOREMHEB: Egypt – great Egypt – to betray those who trust in her.

HIGH PRIEST: [*softly to* HOREMHEB] To see our country brought low – shamed – disgraced –

AKHNATON: Because Egypt is great, all the eyes of the world are upon her and seeing what Egypt does, lesser nations shall follow.

HOREMHEB: They will only say – Egypt is weak! [*Turns away*.]

[*Enter* AY, NEFERTITI *and* NEZZEMUT *and* NUBIAN SERVANT.]

AY: Your Majesty, there is news from the City of No. The people have risen and destroyed the Temple of Aton. They go to and fro in the streets shouting aloud for Amon. The rebellion is fostered by the priests.

HIGH PRIEST: [*coming forward*] That is untrue.

AY: So you are here, Meriptah? Are you mad to venture into this place even disguised?

AKHNATON: [*fanatical*] Amon! The priests of Amon!

HIGH PRIEST: They had no part in it.

HOREMHEB: My lord, the High Priest came to beg me to intercede with you for him since he knew your anger would fall upon him.

AY: The rebellion was the work of the priests, my information is sure.

HIGH PRIEST: Untrue.

AKHNATON: [*after a pause – he is trembling*] I have been patient too long and so has my Father Aton. What has been the curse of this land? The tyranny of Amon. It has enslaved the people, exploited the poor, gorged itself on blood and cruelty. [*Fanatically*] The power of Amon must be cast out root and branch!

HIGH PRIEST: [*melodramatically*] Slay me if you will –

AKHNATON: I do not shed blood. That you should know. [*Loudly*] Let scribes be sent for to take down my words.

[SERVANT *hurries out.*]

AY: [*anxiously*] What is it that you would do, Master? Be careful – do not act in haste.

AKHNATON: I know what must be done.

NEZZEMUT: [*to* HIGH PRIEST] This is risky.

HIGH PRIEST: But successful.

NEFERTITI: Take time to think, Akhnaton. You are not yourself.

AKHNATON: There is an evil power in this land. It shall be stamped out. I will crush the evil of Amon!

[HIGH PRIEST *and* NEZZEMUT *exchange quick glances.*]

HOREMHEB: My lord, do nothing rash. The worship of Amon is old and long established. It brings comfort to many.

AKHNATON: Evil must go!

NEFERTITI: Not in hate, Akhnaton – do nothing in hate.

[SCRIBE *enters.*]

AKHNATON: [*in official voice*] Hear my words, the words of the King of Upper and Lower Egypt, Living in Truth, Lord of the Two Lands.

[*Pause.* SCRIBE *writes.*]

This is my will – that the worship of Amon be no longer permitted, that the name of Amon wheresoever it occurs throughout the Land of Egypt shall be erased. On every monument – and on every inscription throughout the land the name of Amon shall be blotted out.

HOREMHEB: [*in protest*] My lord . . .

AKHNATON: [*with rising voice*] And it is my command that my servants shall enter the tombs of the dead and erase the name of Amon.

HOREMHEB: [*appalled*] But your own father's name!

AKHNATON: My father's name shall not be spared. Let it be erased with the rest.

AY: This is sacrilege!

[*There is a murmur from all.*]

AKHNATON: [*to* SCRIBE] Go. Let my commands be carried out forthwith.

[SCRIBE *hurries out.* MERIPTAH, *pretending to be utterly crushed, follows.*

NEZZEMUT *retires into background and watches the others, who crowd round* AKHNATON.]

HOREMHEB: My lord, you cannot do this! It will antagonize the whole land. It is bad policy. The consequences may be serious in the extreme.

AKHNATON: [*shaking with emotion*] The name of Amon shall be wiped out of Egypt!

AY: There is no wisdom in this course. You will defeat your own object. And to deface the inscriptions in the tombs . . . [*Shakes his head.*]

NEFERTITI: Your own father's name! Akhnaton, you cannot do it.

AY: Be advised, my son. The hearts of the people will turn – not to the Aton, but back to Amon. And the sacrilege of your father's name . . . [*Shakes his head.*] God knows what will come of it all.

AKHNATON: Words – all words. There is one evil, and one evil only in this land, [*his face quivers*] the power of the priesthood of Amon. I know – none better – I grew up in its shadow. This is the war, Horemheb, the real war that must be fought. Between Light and Darkness, between Truth and Falsehood – between Life and Death. Amon and the priests of Amon are the dark power that strangle the Land of Egypt. I will deliver my land. I will bring it from darkness into light – the Eternal Light of the ever-living God. From now on the battle is between me and the priests. And Light shall conquer Darkness.

[*Flings up his arms and staggers over to couch.*]

HOREMHEB: [*as though in a dream*] Egypt – what will become of you? Egypt . . .

CURTAIN

ACT THREE *Scene One*

SCENE: *The King's Pavilion in the City of the Horizon. Three years later.*

AKHNATON, NEFERTITI *and* TUTANKHATON *are together. The* KING *lies on couch R. He is much altered, looks ill and wild-eyed.*

The SCRIBE *sits to take down words.*

AKHNATON: Write. [*A pause.*] The sweet breath which comes from the mouth of Aton – the sweet breath – I breathe it – it is in me – [*Sighs.*] How hot it is, how airless!

NEFERTITI: It is the scorching wind from the south.

AKHNATON: [*wearily*] The wind of death – it scorches and blisters – it denies life.

NEFERTITI: It will change. Soon it will blow sweetly from the north. [*She strokes his forehead.*]

AKHNATON: [*repeating like a child*] Sweetly – from the north – cool [*holds up her hands*] as thy sweet hands are cool. [*To the* SCRIBE] Write. [*Raises himself on his elbow – with a touch of frenzy.*] I desire to hear thy sweet voice, O my Father Aton – thy sweet voice, even the north wind, that my limbs may be rejuvenated with life – rejuvenated with life – through love of thee. [*Wearily*] My limbs rejuvenated – [*Sobs.*]

NEFERTITI: What is it, my dear lord? What is it?

AKHNATON: They will not come – the words of my vision – my limbs are too weary.

NEFERTITI: When the heat of summer passes you will grow strong again.

AKHNATON: Shall I? [*Plays with her hands.*] Shall I model once more in clay – and paint with delicate colours? Now I am too tired.

NEFERTITI: You must rest.

AKHNATON: So tired that even words will not come to me . . . [*stroking her hands*] Sweet hands – sweet hands – [*With sudden burst of inspiration*] Give me thy hands, O Aton, holding thy spirit, that I may receive it and live by it . . .

[*He is transfixed by ecstasy.* NEFERTITI *draws her hands away with a sudden gesture.*

HOREMHEB *enters and stops.*]

[*rapt*] Thy spirit, that I may live by it . . .

NEFERTITI: Would you speak with the King, Lord Horemheb?

HOREMHEB: There is news from Syria.

NEFERTITI: Not now. The King is weary in the Great Heat. He must not be disturbed.

HOREMHEB: For seven days now that is the answer that is given to the messengers. Messengers who have ridden night and day, desperate with the urgency of life and death. And they are told – The King is sleeping – The King is sailing on his lake – The King is praying to the Aton. Shall I then tell them plainly once and for all The King has no time to give to his subjects?

AKHNATON: [*coming out of his vision*] Is that my dear Horemheb?

[NEFERTITI *moves back unwillingly.*]

HOREMHEB: It is I, sir. I have urgent news. But perhaps I shall interrupt a poem. Some poem of great beauty made for the Queen!

NEFERTITI: [*with a trace of bitterness*] It was not made for me.

AKHNATON: It is a hymn to my Father Aton. A hymn that shall be engraved on my tomb.

TUTANKHATON: Oh, Father-in-law. Do not speak as though you were going to die.

AKHNATON: One must be prepared for Death, Son. That has always been the belief of Egypt. Horemheb, here, built his tomb many years ago. Soon we will begin to prepare yours. Mine is cut and decorated awaiting me. But it is not only the resting place one must prepare, it is the soul.

HOREMHEB: It is of bodies I would speak, my lord, if you could turn your mind from souls.

AKHNATON: Tell me, then.

HOREMHEB: [*reading from a roll of papyrus*] From the Governor of your City of Tunip by the Land of Mitanni. To the King of Egypt, my Lord. The inhabitants of Tunip, thy servant. May it be well with thee. At the feet of our Lord we fall. Tunip, thy servant, speaks saying 'Who formerly could have plundered Tunip without being plundered by Thutmosis the King?' For truly the Gods of Egypt dwell in Tunip! May the King ask of his old men if it be not so. But now the King of Egypt forsakes us and no longer protects us. If his soldiers and chariots come not, Aziru the Amorite will make us like the City of No. He will do to us as he pleases in the territory of our Lord the King. Tunip, thy city, weeps and her tears are flowing and there is no help for us. For many years we have been sending to our Lord the King, the King of Egypt, but there has come to us not a word – no, not one.

[*There is a long pause.*]

AKHNATON: My poor city.

HOREMHEB: Their faith is still in us. They still hope and believe that Egypt will not let them perish.

AKHNATON: How heavy is my burden.

HOREMHEB: My lord, it is not too late. Byblos and Simyra are still loyal. We can disembark troops at these ports, march inland to Tunip. Dushratta, the King of Mitanni, is loyal. Though Itakama, the King of Kadesh, has joined hands with the Hittites, yet our forces can crush him easily and then Aziru will easily be dealt with.

AKHNATON: Will you never understand that force is not the way to peace?

HOREMHEB: Ribaddi writes saying Simyra is like a bird in a snare. [*Pause.*] My lord, Ribaddi is my friend, splendid, staunch, a man in a thousand. Will you condemn him and his sons to death?

AKHNATON: You do not know what you are asking. To go back to the old ways – the old evil ways of death – mutilation – violence. It must not be . . .

HOREMHEB: Askalon and Gezer, and the City of Lachish

have thrown off the Egyptian yoke. Listen to this despatch from your servant Abdikhiba. [*Reads.*] The King's whole land will be lost. Behold the territory of Seir as far as Carmel, its Princes are lost and hostility prevails against me. Let my Lord take care of his land and let him send troops. For if no troops come in the year the whole territory of my Lord the King will perish. [*Pause.*] And this good soldier ends his letter thus: If there are no troops within the year let the King send his officer to fetch me and my brothers that we may die with our Lord the King.

AKHNATON: Write, Scribe. Take down these my words to my servant, Aziru. I have heard evil accounts of thee and that thou dost oppress and harry my loyal servants and cities. I command thee therefore to come to this my City of the Horizon and answer to me for the deeds which it is said you have committed. Thou hast professed to me to love the Aton and to embrace peace and good will. Come, therefore, and prove thy words.

HOREMHEB: Useless! He will reply with an Oriental's cunning words of lying and flattery, that he is loyal to Egypt, that he does indeed embrace the new teaching and meanwhile the cities that trust in us and the men who believe will be destroyed utterly.

NEFERTITI: [*angrily*] You forget yourself, Horemheb. It is the King who speaks – the Son of Ra. Who lives in Truth.

AKHNATON: Do not blame him, Nefertiti. It is love for his friends that makes him speak thus.

HOREMHEB: [*brokenly*] Oh my dear lord, I beg of you, by

any love you bear to me, send help to the men who trust in you.

AKHNATON: Listen, Horemheb, if these poor ignorant men run wild and kill each other, and harry and oppress, it will be forgiven them because they know no better. But it would not be forgiven Me . . . By no word of mine shall blood be shed. For that is the command of my Father the Aton . . . Till the swan shall turn black and the crow turn white, till the hills rise up to travel and the deeps rush into the rivers, I will do the will of my Father.

[HOREMHEB *turns away groaning.*]

[*coming over to him*] Dear friend, try to understand.

[HOREMHEB *turns away.*]

HOREMHEB: I cannot.

[AKHNATON *sighs and turns back to* NEFERTITI *and* TUTANKHATON.]

AKHNATON: Let us walk by the trees. It may be cooler there.

[AKHNATON *goes out,* NEFERTITI *and* TUTANKHATON *with him.*

NEZZEMUT *watches* HOREMHEB *who is lost in despondency.*]

NEZZEMUT: [*forcibly*] Do you realize, at last, that the King is mad?

HOREMHEB: [*startled*] Mad?

NEZZEMUT: Yes, his brain is affected. Religion does drive people mad – unless it is organized and controlled like the worship of Amon was.

HOREMHEB: I cannot bear it.

NEZZEMUT: There will be worse to come. [*Watches him carefully.*] Such madness increases rapidly –

HOREMHEB: The King? My dear, dear lord – mad?

NEZZEMUT: [*impatiently*] I cannot think why you have not seen it before. I have for a long while.

HOREMHEB: [*realizing her for the first time*] You, Princess?

NEZZEMUT: I am not entirely taken up with frivolous matters. It may seem strange to you, but I care for my country. I do not like to see Egypt become the laughing-stock of a host of impertinent little nations.

[HOREMHEB *winces.*]

Making fools of ourselves for the Syrians and the Nubians and the Hittites to jeer at.

HOREMHEB: Please –

NEZZEMUT: If you are a soldier you ought to be prepared to admit the truth. What path has Egypt trod in the last fifteen years?

HOREMHEB: True . . .

NEZZEMUT: I love my country. I rejoiced in her greatness. She could be great again. It is not too late.

HOREMHEB: It soon will be.

NEZZEMUT: Yes, it soon will be . . . [*significantly*] unless something is done.

HOREMHEB: What can anyone do? The King – my dear lord – Amon help him – is mad.

NEZZEMUT: You admit that?

HOREMHEB: Yes.

NEZZEMUT: There is only one person who can save Egypt – you, Horemheb.

HOREMHEB: I?

NEZZEMUT: Yes, you have enormous influence over the people. They worship you. And you have the Army behind you. You are the only man in Egypt with power and ability. Who else is there in this Court of ours?

HOREMHEB: Artists, Amon help us! Sculptors! Musicians! Dancers! An unreal world given over to pleasure.

NEZZEMUT: And you the only real person in it!

HOREMHEB: [*simply, without vanity*] It does seem like that to me sometimes.

NEZZEMUT: Is all this like a nightmare to you?

HOREMHEB: Yes.

NEZZEMUT: Then act, man, for Amon's sake, act!

HOREMHEB: What do you mean?

NEZZEMUT: You are a man of action. Will you sit down with your head in your hands and despair?

HOREMHEB: Show me a straight path and I would take it. As it is, my hands are tied.

NEZZEMUT: Egypt lies at the mercy of a madman – dear to you, to me, to us all – but still a madman.

HOREMHEB: No country should be in the power of one man. It is crazy. [*Strides up and down.*]

NEZZEMUT: [*lowering her voice after a quick look round*] I have a message for you.

HOREMHEB: For me?

NEZZEMUT: From Meriptah, High Priest of Amon.

HOREMHEB: What is it?

NEZZEMUT: He bids you remember certain words. He bids you ask yourself a question. Which should come first with a man – his King or his country?

HOREMHEB: They are the same.

NEZZEMUT: Not always. Are they the same today?

[AKHNATON *enters.*]

AKHNATON: Leave me, Nezzemut. I would talk with Horemheb alone.

[*Exit* NEZZEMUT.

AKHNATON *comes over to* HOREMHEB.]

[*with emotion*] My dearest friend.

HOREMHEB: My dear, dear lord. [*Almost breaks down.*]

AKHNATON: Most faithful heart! You do not understand, but your love is unchanged!

HOREMHEB: Unchanged – unchanged –

AKHNATON: [*with great emphasis*] But you *must* understand – you must! I must find words to show you. Beauty, Truth, Love, Peace – do you not see, these things are eternal – more important than the births and deaths and suffering of men's bodies.

HOREMHEB: Birth and Death and Suffering are facts – the others are Words.

AKHNATON: [*sighing*] It is the same now as at the beginning – long ago – in my father's Palace. Our minds and understanding set far from each other. Why, then, is there this love between us?

HOREMHEB: To torture us, perhaps.

AKHNATON: [*wistfully*] I was so young then – so full of hope. Life seemed so easy – the way so clear. To give love and peace to my people. And they will have none of it. Strange. And even my friends here – my disciples – those whom I have taught. [*Angrily*] Do you know what they seek to do, Horemheb? They wish to make a vast image of the Aton – a stone monster like the old foolish Gods – like Hathor, like Ptah – [*with venom*] like Amon. That is all they know of Him who is the Living Light. To make a stone image and pen it in a temple. And they are my children brought up in the new wisdom, seeing nothing, hearing nothing, understanding nothing – understanding nothing. Does no one understand – not even Nefertiti – does no one understand but me? [*Softly*] Is that what it means to be the Son of God? [*His hands uplifted – he stands in a trance.*]

HOREMHEB: My lord, my dear lord. You are sick. You are weary.

AKHNATON: [*childishly*] Yes, I am sick – it is too much to bear, this burden. I am weary – so weary.

HOREMHEB: You must have rest. Could you not rest altogether – live here in your beautiful city and leave the cares of state to another?

AKHNATON: How could that be?

HOREMHEB: You could associate an heir with you as Joint Ruler – it has been done before.

AKHNATON: I have no heir. No son to come after me. [*To Heaven*] Why, O Aton, why have I no son?

HOREMHEB: The husband of one of your daughters could

rule with you as is the custom. The lad Tutankhaton is a likely Prince. Let him marry Ankhepaaton, your daughter, to whom he is betrothed, and then let him rule with you.

AKHNATON: My elder daughter's husband, Smenkhara, should come first. He is a true lover of Aton, full of ecstasy and vision.

HOREMHEB: But he is sickly – his health is bad. Tutankhaton is young and strong.

AKHNATON: Could a boy like that rule Egypt?

HOREMHEB: Make me his Vizier . . .

AKHNATON: [*slowly*] It may not be. The burden is mine. I may not give it over to another. I must go on – to the end. [*He drops his head in his hands.*]

[NEFERTITI *enters.*]

NEFERTITI: Will you not come and rest? Must you forever be talking of state matters? [*Angrily to* HOREMHEB] Can you not see that he is ill – that he is unfit to be worried?

HOREMHEB: I do see that.

AKHNATON: [*bewildered, his speech slurred*] There was something – something. Something that must be done at once.

NEFERTITI: Not now.

AKHNATON: An image – an image of Aton. Are the people blind? Are they wilfully stupid?

NEFERTITI: Do not worry about that. You have told them it is not to be.

AKHNATON: Yes, but they should see for themselves – [*Stops suddenly and looks piercingly at her.*] Do *you* see?

NEFERTITI: Do I see what?

AKHNATON: How impossible it is that there should be an image made of God.

NEFERTITI: [*slightly worried*] If you do not wish it –

AKHNATON: That is not the point. I must know – I must know – this is very important. [*He is unstrung.*]

NEFERTITI: [*soothingly*] Tell me exactly what it is you want to know.

AKHNATON: Does it seem to you possible that an image could ever be made of God?

NEFERTITI: It would have to be very beautiful. [*Thoughtfully*] I do not think any of your sculptors are great enough.

AKHNATON: [*turning away and groaning*] Alone – alone – I am quite alone. You too . . .

NEFERTITI: I, too – For you there is only the Aton.

AKHNATON: It is so clear – so clear and yet they cannot see it. [*Rocks to and fro. Suddenly looking up*] In the past Amon was called the King of the Gods, was he not?

NEFERTITI: Yes – but that is all over now. Amon is not worshipped any more.

AKHNATON: No – no – Ah yes, now I see – that is what must be done. [*He is silent a long time, his eyes staring.*]

NEFERTITI: What is it, my dear lord?

AKHNATON: [*raising his head and stretching up his hands*] Why have you left me, my Father Aton? I no longer feel your life running through me. I am alone – alone.

[*Takes a few steps, sways and nearly falls as though with a slight seizure.* NEFERTITI *and* HOREMHEB *run to him and guide him to couch.*]

NEFERTITI: The King is sick. Send for the physicians.

AKHNATON: No, it is nothing. [*Sits up.*] I see now – I must do more – more. Nefertiti –

NEFERTITI: Yes, dear lord.

AKHNATON: Listen, Nefertiti, our Father Aton is not the King of the Gods – if he were you could make an image of him. He is not the King of the Gods because there are no other Gods. He is God himself. And so, you see, these other crude images must go. Yes, that is what is wrong. I thought only of Amon, of the tyranny of Amon. But *all* the Gods must go. Then, at last, the people will begin to see and understand the true meaning and essence of God . . . [*Closes his eyes. Opens them and speaks briskly.*] Horemheb, see that my commands are carried out. Throughout Egypt the names of all Gods are to be erased and wiped out, Hathor, Ptah of Memphis, Osiris, Isis, Sekhmet, Annubis . . .

HOREMHEB: But my lord, it is impossible. The people would not stand it.

NEFERTITI: No, no, Akhnaton. Hathor brings comfort to ignorant women and peasants, and Osiris comforts the poor when their loved ones die.

AKHNATON: They must go – all of them.

NEFERTITI: No, no, do not take from people anything that brings them comfort and help.

AKHNATON: One must take away that which is false. Only Truth matters – Eternal and Living Truth.

NEFERTITI: Everyone cannot live in Truth as you do.

HOREMHEB: Indeed, sir, such a course would be unwise.

AKHNATON: They must go – they must go – [*springing up*

wildly in a frenzy] Everything must go that stands between man and the living Truth of God.

NEFERTITI: Then I too must go – Erase my name as you will erase your father's! [*In wild anger*] I renounce the Aton. Do you hear? I renounce the Aton.

[AKHNATON *staggers and falls.*]

[*Runs to him.*] Akhnaton – Akhnaton –

HOREMHEB: Nezzemut was right. The King is mad.

CURTAIN

ACT THREE *Scene Two*

SCENE: *A Street in Thebes. Six months later.*

On the corner stand two MEN *wrapped in cloaks,* HOREMHEB *and the* HIGH PRIEST *pressed against the wall.*

Two WOMEN *enter.*

FIRST WOMAN: Not so fast. I am too weak.

SECOND WOMAN: Courage, it is not far now.

FIRST WOMAN: I would as soon die here on the street. My son is dead and gone to Osiris.

SECOND WOMAN: Hush, one mustn't mention Osiris now.

FIRST WOMAN: Gentle Osiris who pleads for the dead. Where are our dead now with no Osiris to plead for them?

SECOND WOMAN: The Gods have left Egypt. They are angry.

FIRST WOMAN: Who is this new God? What has he done for us?

> [*She stumbles.* MAN *enters from opposite side. He comes quickly and helps support her.*]

MAN: Hold up, Mother.

SECOND WOMAN: She is weak for want of food.

FIRST WOMAN: They took all I had – everything – beans – onions –

MAN: There's no justice any longer.

SECOND WOMAN: Hush, be careful. My son complained – the tax-gatherers beat him over the head. He's been queer ever since. He's like a little child.

[MAN *shakes his head. The two* WOMEN *pass on.*]

FIRST WOMAN: [*as they go off*] Osiris – gentle Osiris . . .

[*Another* MAN *enters.*]

SECOND MAN: Poor old soul.

FIRST MAN: They're dying like flies. The Gods are angry with Egypt.

SECOND MAN: This year there's been nothing but misfortune.

FIRST MAN: First the locusts –

SECOND MAN: And then the water falling from the sky. That hasn't happened for fifty years.

FIRST MAN: It's the closing of the temples.

SECOND MAN: The end of the world is coming, so they say.

FIRST MAN: I shouldn't be surprised. How odd it seems to think we were once happy – and prosperous too. My wine was famous!

SECOND MAN: I remember. Oh well, the good times won't come back.

FIRST MAN: Do you remember when they carried Amon through the streets?

SECOND MAN: The processions –

FIRST MAN: The singing –

SECOND MAN: Amon – the Vizier of the poor.

FIRST MAN: And now you daren't mention the name of Amon.

SECOND MAN: The King even cut his own father's name out of the tomb.

FIRST MAN: [*slowly nodding his head*] A man who'd do that would do anything.

SECOND MAN: He isn't a man – he's a King.

FIRST MAN: King or no King, Amon curse him!

SECOND MAN: Hush!

FIRST MAN: [*recklessly*] Things can't be worse. He's brought us to this. All those fine words and proclamations about peace and good will –

[*They go off together.*]

HIGH PRIEST: [*to* HOREMHEB] Have you heard enough?

HOREMHEB: Yes, I have heard enough.

HIGH PRIEST: Ruin and misery stalk through the land and the spirit of the people is broken. Think of Egypt fifteen years ago.

HOREMHEB: Don't remind me.

HIGH PRIEST: Two more cities have fallen in Syria and their garrisons put to the sword.

HOREMHEB: I know. The Khabiri sweep through the lands killing and slaying as they go.

HIGH PRIEST: Egypt has fallen very low.

HOREMHEB: The shame of it!

HIGH PRIEST: What of the soldiers?

HOREMHEB: Chafing to be allowed to come to the rescue of their friends across the sea.

125

HIGH PRIEST: But it is not too late.

HOREMHEB: By Amon, no! Give me two years – less – and Egypt shall raise her head again.

HIGH PRIEST: Come.

CURTAIN

ACT THREE *Scene Three*

SCENE: *A room in the High Priest's house in Thebes. The same day.*

There is a window centre. Entrance L.

The HIGH PRIEST, NEZZEMUT, TUTANKHATON *and* HOREMHEB *sit round a table.* HOREMHEB *is morose, lost in thought.*

HIGH PRIEST: In the main, then, we are agreed?

NEZZEMUT: Agreed.

HIGH PRIEST: For the sake of our country it is resolved that the King Amenhotep IV called Akhnaton must cease to reign? This we decide in no spirit of rebellion but for the good and lasting peace of Egypt.

NEZZEMUT AND TUTANKHATON: Yes.

HIGH PRIEST: [*to* TUTANKHATON] To you, my lord, we offer fealty and the double Crown of Egypt, your title to it being through your wife, the Royal Lady Ankhep-aaton. Do you swear that you will uphold the well-being of our country?

TUTANKHATON: That I swear.

HIGH PRIEST: And that, once the double crown rests securely upon your head, you will restore to Egypt the worship of Amon and other Gods and that you will repair and restore the Temples of Amon?

TUTANKHATON: I swear to restore the worship of Amon.

HIGH PRIEST: And that you will, in due course, abandon

the name of Tutankhaton and take instead that of Tutankhamun?

TUTANKHATON: Yes.

HIGH PRIEST: Then I, Meriptah, High Priest of Amon, in the name of Amon, swear that the priesthood of Amon will support your claim. From the treasure house of Amon gold shall be supplied for your funeral furniture and all shall be done to make you a great and puissant King.

> [TUTANKHATON *bows his head, pleased and boyishly excited.*]

> [*to* NEZZEMUT] To you, Royal Lady, I offer the title of High Priestess, Divine Consort of Amon, as was the late Queen Tyi – the highest title that Amon can offer, and with it control of the Royal Dowry of the Consort of the God.

> [NEZZEMUT *bows her head.*]

> It is for you to speak now, my Lord Horemheb. Without you we can do nothing. Are you with us in this matter?

> [HOREMHEB *is silent.*]

> Come, my lord, the fate of Egypt is at stake.

TUTANKHATON: My lord, do not fail me. Without you I must surely fail.

HOREMHEB: [*slowly*] It is understood that the King – Akhnaton – shall remain in his City of the Horizon and there be treated with all honour?

HIGH PRIEST: It is agreed.

HOREMHEB: [*gets up and paces up and down*] Is there no other way?

NEZZEMUT: No.

HOREMHEB: [*brokenly*] His trust in me . . . his love . . . never failing . . .

HIGH PRIEST: Simyra has fallen – Byblos has been put to the sword . . . The treasury is empty – Egypt is bankrupt . . . The gold mines are no longer worked – no foreign tribute comes in – soon the land will starve and decay . . .

[HOREMHEB *groans*.]

NEZZEMUT: Come here.

[*Leads him to window C. Draws curtains and he steps on to balcony. A great roar goes up outside.*]

CROWD: Horemheb . . . Horemheb . . .

[*He staggers back from window. She draws curtains again.*]

HIGH PRIEST: You have heard the voice of Egypt. Egypt trusts you. Which way will you choose – that of a personal love, a personal loyalty, or the broader way of patriotism?

HOREMHEB: [*his head up*] I choose – my country.

[*Goes out abruptly L.*

HIGH PRIEST *and* NEZZEMUT *heave a sigh of relief.*]

NEZZEMUT: Up to the end I feared.

HIGH PRIEST: Mercifully it has ended well. [*To* TUTAN-
KHATON] My lord, it would be well, I think, if you
followed Lord Horemheb and distracted his sad thoughts.

TUTANKHATON: I will go and find him.

HIGH PRIEST: Farewell – O King.

[TUTANKHATON *goes out.*

NEZZEMUT *and* HIGH PRIEST *look at each other.*]

At last! You have done good work, daughter. You have
a shrewd and ambitious brain.

NEZZEMUT: I expect my reward.

HIGH PRIEST: It will not be long delayed. One cannot hurry
matters.

NEZZEMUT: I suppose not.

HIGH PRIEST: [*after a pause*] Shall we be explicit?

NEZZEMUT: By all means.

HIGH PRIEST: The boy, as you realize, is only a figurehead.
Horemheb will be the ruling power in Egypt.

NEZZEMUT: That is not enough for me.

HIGH PRIEST: [*choosing his words with deliberate significance*]
In a year or two it may chance that the boy will sicken
and die. In fact, I think it is almost sure to happen –

NEZZEMUT: Two years?

HIGH PRIEST: We must go slowly. Horemheb himself
must be brought to the idea. To supplant Akhnaton – he
would never hear of it. But if the boy were gradually
to pine and sicken – [*pause*] it can be managed – then the
people would unanimously declare for Horemheb. The
statue of Amon carried in procession will halt and bow

to him. He will accept the will of the Gods and of the people. To consolidate his claim to the throne and that all may be done decently and in order, he must marry a Lady of the Royal Blood, the Divine Consort of Amon.

NEZZEMUT: Ah!

HIGH PRIEST: That is my side of the bargain. [*Significantly*] Now for yours. Horemheb still yearns to the heretic. While Akhnaton lives – [*pause*] we can never be sure of Horemheb.

NEZZEMUT: The King is already a sick man. Since Nefertiti left him, he weakens and pines. If he were to die suddenly – a seizure – [*She smiles significantly.*]

HIGH PRIEST: You can promise that?

NEZZEMUT: My dwarf Para knows the secret of preparing sudden death.

HIGH PRIEST: May Amon prosper the undertaking! [*With exultation*] Soon the temples will be restored to their full glory and Amon will reign once more in his city. The heresy of Akhnaton will be wiped out from human memory.

NEZZEMUT: No harm must happen to my sister, Queen Nefertiti. Her name has been effaced – she is no longer Royal. But she may return to Akhnaton.

HIGH PRIEST: No harm shall befall her.

NEZZEMUT: She will be no anxiety to you. She is a gentle creature. She will mourn for Akhnaton and not bother her head with politics. She has no spirit.

HIGH PRIEST: You are a clever woman, Nezzemut.

NEZZEMUT: I return the compliment. You are a clever man.

Is it only Akhnaton's incompetence that has brought about the demoralization of this city?

HIGH PRIEST: [*smiling*] Oh! We priests have our methods. Like moles, we work underground. Organization, that's the secret – organization.

NEZZEMUT: The old Queen was right to fear you.

HIGH PRIEST: [*quite the unctuous prelate*] It is perhaps fortunate for us that her son did not inherit her distrustful nature.

NEZZEMUT: Did he ever have a chance against you, I wonder?

HIGH PRIEST: If he had met cunning with cunning, intrigue with intrigue. [*Shakes his head.*] But he chose open warfare. [*Scornfully*] The fool! To pit himself against the might of Amon and his priests.

CURTAIN

ACT THREE *Scene Four*

SCENE: *A room in the King's Palace – a few weeks later.*

The KING *sits wearily on a great gold chair up R.* NEFERTITI *sits on a stool beside him. There is a window down R. and a couch, and an entrance up L.*

The bust of NEFERTITI *stands on a pedestal.*

TIME: *It is late afternoon.*

Enter BEK.

BEK: My lord, I have been to the treasurer to get gold for the purchase of stone and other materials. The treasury, he says, is empty.

AKHNATON: Empty? How can it be empty?

BEK: There is no foreign tribute coming in. The tax-gatherers no longer remit any taxes. The gold mines are not being worked.

AKHNATON: Have we spent all the gold of Egypt?

BEK: It looks like it.

AKHNATON: But Egypt is rich – her crops – her gold – where is Horemheb?

BEK: He has not yet returned.

AKHNATON: Alone – I am alone.

NEFERTITI: Go now, good Bek, the King is weary. [*To* AKHNATON] I am with you – here beside you.

[BEK *goes*.]

AKHNATON: No tribute from Syria – and no news. What has happened there?

NEFERTITI: Do not think about it.

AKHNATON: My people – my poor people. [*To* NEFERTITI] Do you think I ought –

NEFERTITI: Ought what?

AKHNATON: Nothing. Why does not Horemheb return?

NEFERTITI: Rats leave a sinking ship.

AKHNATON: Horemheb is not a rat.

NEFERTITI: Yet he is gone to the City of No – not to his province in the north.

AKHNATON: [*smiling*] You shall not make me doubt. Horemheb is Truth and Loyalty itself.

NEFERTITI: It may be so.

AKHNATON: How long it seems since that day I first saw him. In the courtyard of my father's Palace. He was with the High Priest of Amon. It was then, in one short hour, that our love for each other ripened and has never failed.

NEFERTITI: Why should you so love this man – this stupid brutal soldier who cares nothing for Art or Sculpture or Beauty – who cannot understand your thoughts or share your visions?

AKHNATON: Love is always a mystery.

NEFERTITI: It would be better if you had never seen that man.

AKHNATON: Why do you say that?

NEFERTITI: I have always feared him.

AKHNATON: My foolish, beautiful one.

NEFERTITI: Am I still that to you?

AKHNATON: Foolish – or beautiful?

NEFERTITI: Both. I was never very wise.

AKHNATON: Your wisdom is of the heart – deep and profound. Your beauty too. It lies not only in the turn of your cheek bone – in the texture of your skin . . .

NEFERTITI: I am no longer beautiful. I am the mother of many daughters. My face grows weary and lined. My body has lost its first grace and harmony.

AKHNATON: You are to me Beauty's self – the only loved woman of Akhnaton the King – perfect in beauty for ever.

NEFERTITI: [*with feeling*] Then let me die now before beauty departs from me, before I grow old and worn and the eyes of the King no longer rest with pleasure on my beauty. So shall I live for ever in the memories of men as young and fair and beloved.

AKHNATON: So shall they see you carved in stone standing by my side in my Palace and on the walls of the temples I have built.

NEFERTITI: Palaces crumble and temples fall to decay. In time to come none shall know how Nefertiti the Queen looked – my very name will be forgotten.

[*Enter* SERVANT.]

SERVANT: The Lord Horemheb is here and would speak with the King.

AKHNATON: Send him here at once.

[*Exit* SERVANT.]

Did I not tell you Horemheb was no rat?

[NEFERTITI *shrugs her shoulders.*

Enter HOREMHEB. *He is stern and aloof. He makes a formal obeisance.*]

AKHNATON: Welcome, dear friend. I began to be anxious at your long absence. But now it is joy indeed to see your face once more.

HOREMHEB: It is no joyful words I come to speak.

AKHNATON: What has happened?

HOREMHEB: [*with irony*] Things that are doubtless of no account to you, O King. Ribaddi your faithful servant is dead. His possessions were reft from him, his lands devastated, his sons and his brother were killed round him. He died, loyal to the last to a King who took no heed of his misery.

AKHNATON: Not so – not so . . .

HOREMHEB: Egypt is shamed by his death. To be an Egyptian today is to walk humbly bowing beneath the scorn of countries that trusted in our word. Throughout Syria is the land of the Two Rivers, in the land of Canaan, in Kadesh and Mitanni, everywhere the enemies of Egypt triumph – the wild Khabiri overrun the land putting all to the sword. Our garrisons have held out and been slaughtered at their posts. You, O King, who would shed no blood, are stained for ever by the blood of your own people and those who trusted in you.

AKHNATON: [*moaning*] Cruel – cruel –

HOREMHEB: I, too, am stained with that blood. I, Commander-in-Chief of the Army of Egypt, have sat with folded hands and let old friends, old allies, perish and go to their deaths cursing Egypt. I have sat in Palaces, and lived soft and easily, and watched dancing and heard music – all this to my shame. But now –

NEFERTITI: [*alertly*] What now, Horemheb?

HOREMHEB: [*slowly*] Now, my lord the King, our ways part. Egypt is ruined – in chaos, her people distraught and perplexed, deprived of their Gods like dumb beasts not knowing which way to turn. Shall I sit idle any longer? It may be that it is not too late, that order may still be brought out of chaos, that trust and faith in Egypt may be restored abroad. What a man can do, that I must try and accomplish. But not without first speaking to you face to face. This is farewell, sir. [*Pause.*] Forgive me for what I am about to do.

AKHNATON: [*with anguish*] You, Horemheb – you. You whose love for me I have never doubted?

HOREMHEB: I told you before, sir, you trust too much! Every man has his breaking-point.

AKHNATON: Your love for me is dead?

HOREMHEB: [*coldly*] No. But between us are dead men and ravished cities and the name of Egypt brought low. In the end, although you are the King, you are only one man. It is Egypt that matters. My country!

AKHNATON: So narrow a view. It is not one country that matters – it is the world! I love, not only Egypt, but the whole world.

HOREMHEB: Words! For years I have been smothered with words! Deeds, not words, that is what is needed.

AKHNATON: [*with a flash of the old irony*] You were always the man of action!

HOREMHEB: [*with dignity*] I am made that way. We all are as we are made.

NEFERTITI: The priests of Amon will doubtless reward you.

HOREMHEB: It is no question of reward. [*Hesitates.*] Farewell, my lord!

AKHNATON: Farewell.

[HOREMHEB *pauses, then goes out.*]

NEFERTITI: So – a rat after all.

AKHNATON: [*sitting as one paralysed, whispering to himself*] Horemheb – Horemheb – [*Makes groping gesture.*] Gone – all gone . . .

NEFERTITI: Dear lord. Beloved husband.

AKHNATON: [*putting her from him as though in a dream and rising to his feet, walking with groping footsteps – his arms outstretched*] Alone – quite alone . . .

NEFERTITI: [*following him, frightened*] Akhnaton.

AKHNATON: [*raising his hands to Heaven*] I alone knew thy Will on earth, O Father. I was thy Will . . . What am I now? What am I now?

[NEFERTITI *shrinks back. She watches him.*]

When thou settest, O Aton, the world is in darkness. In darkness like the dead. The heads of men are wrapped up, their nostrils stopped and none seeth the other. Stolen are all the things that are under their heads while they know it not. Every lion cometh forth from his den. [*With anguished bitterness*] All serpents they sting. Darkness reigns . . . [*Pause.*] The world is in silence . . .

> [*He drops down on couch and stares ahead of him. Enter* AY. *He has become very old and shaky.* NEFERTITI *comes over to him. They whisper together down L. Then* NEFERTITI *comes back to* AKHNATON.]

NEFERTITI: [*timidly*] My lord?

> [AKHNATON *does not answer.*]

My lord –

> [*She glances at* AY. *They hesitate for a moment.* NEFERTITI *kneels beside her husband, touching his arm.*]

Dear lord –

AKHNATON: [*stirring as though waking*] Yes?

NEFERTITI: Our son-in-law, Tutankhaton, has not returned. He has taken with him all his possessions.

AKHNATON: Where has he gone?

NEFERTITI: To the City of No.

AKHNATON: Tutankhaton also. That dear lad whom we loved. [*Suddenly, to* AY] Speak, there is more to come.

AY: In the City of No a revolt has arisen. The priests of Amon have come out of hiding. They and their followers have seized the city.

AKHNATON: The priests of Amon.

[*A long pause.*]

[*To* AY] What have I done, Father? What have I left undone? Have I done evil to any man? Have I plundered the poor? Have I denied justice? Is it a crime to love Beauty? Is it a crime to desire Peace?

[AY *shakes his head sadly.*]

I loved my people. I wanted them to live in freedom – to dwell together in love and peace and happiness. And instead they must kill each other and rob and cheat and steal and lay waste the kindly earth. Why, old man? Tell me why they do these things?

AY: I do not know . . . I do not know . . . It is, I think, because it is in their hearts so to do.

[*He goes out, shaking his head.*]

AKHNATON: [*clinging wildly to* NEFERTITI] Nefertiti, Nefertiti, is it true – is it true what Horemheb said? Is this blood, this suffering on *my* head? Should I have sent troops when he asked me? Should I? Should I?

NEFERTITI: No.

AKHNATON: All that blood – on my head.

NEFERTITI: [*more firmly*] No.

AKHNATON: [*childishly*] You say that – to comfort me.

NEFERTITI: No, I know it. It is true what Ay said – these people did what they had it in their hearts to do. It must always be so. The old ways – the well-tried, safe ways – the ways that Horemheb knows are not for you. You, too, had to follow what was in your heart – the ways

140

of a new world – of a new life – something that is to come –

AKHNATON: It will come?

NEFERTITI: It will come.

AKHNATON: [*springing to his feet*] By the living Aton – I am the Truth. [*To Heaven*] I am he who knows thy heart. [*His eyeballs roll, he sways – then laughs suddenly and raucously and hysterically.*] Do you remember, Nefertiti, the day when we founded this fair city? [*Declaims*] The King Living in Truth, Akhnaton whose life is long and the great Royal Wife, his beloved, [*Seizes her hand.*] Mistress of the Two Lands. Nefertiti. Living and flourishing for ever and ever. [*Laughs wildly and falls on to couch.*]

THE CURTAIN IS LOWERED TO DENOTE THE PASSAGE OF TIME

It is now just before sunset. The KING *sits on a gold chair, his eyes dull and glazed.* NEFERTITI *is sitting crouched down beside him. Enter* AY. *He comes anxiously to her and questions her mutely. She shakes her head.*

NEFERTITI: [*low*] He will not eat and drink. I am afraid to rouse him now. He gets so wild and strange.

AY: Shall I send for the physicians?

NEFERTITI: No, what can they do? It is *here* that he suffers.

[*She presses her hand to her head.*]

AY: O Divine Love which is in the Aton restore thy son!

[*Moves towards door L.* NEFERTITI *follows him.*]

NEFERTITI: Is there news?

AY: There are rumours everywhere. What are rumours?

NEFERTITI: Tell me what they say.

AY: They say that both the Upper and Lower Lands have risen. That everywhere the temples are being opened again and rebuilt and the images that were overthrown are being set up again.

NEFERTITI: Oh that! Anything else?

AY: It is said that the great statue of Amon was taken in procession through the City of No –

NEFERTITI: Yes, yes?

AY: The usual priestly trick. It stopped before Tutankhaton.

NEFERTITI: Tutankhaton?

AY: Yes. The Priests of Amon wish to make Tutankhaton King.

NEFERTITI: There can be only one King in Egypt, Akhnaton.

AY: Doubtless the priests will try to make Akhnaton acknowledge Tutankhaton as joint ruler.

NEFERTITI: The King will not do that. This very day he has associated Smenkara with him as joint Pharaoh.

AY: The priests will not accept Smenkara. They know he is filled with the love of Aton. He would never acknowledge Amon or revive his worship.

NEFERTITI: Will the people accept the will of the priests against the will of the King?

AY: That I do not know. There is great reverence felt for the person of the Pharaoh. Even the priesthood cannot wholly prevail against that. Meriptah will have his work cut out.

NEFERTITI: Akhnaton will never yield.

AKHNATON: [*to himself*] Alone – quite alone –

[NEFERTITI *and* AY *are startled.*]

NEFERTITI: What did you say, my dearest lord?
AKHNATON: The Divine Love of the Aton has departed from me. The world is in darkness.

[AY *and* NEFERTITI *look at each other in doubt.*]

NEFERTITI: What can we do?
AY: If he would eat – or drink –
NEFERTITI: He does not hear me when I speak to him.
AY: My heart misgives me. I have advised him ill.
NEFERTITI: What should you have done?
AY: I encouraged him in his ideas. I should have preached moderation, compromise, the wisdom of the serpent. But he was like a young eagle.
NEFERTITI: Yes, that is true . . . A young eagle flying up to the sun. [*Pause.*] Do not blame yourself, Ay. When the eagle flies none can restrain him.

[AY *shakes his head and goes out.*]

In the doorway he encounters NEZZEMUT. *She comes in almost gaily with a somewhat forced manner.* PARA *is with her.*]

NEZZEMUT: Why, what gloom you sit in!
NEFERTITI: [*running to her*] Sister – O Sister. I thought you had deserted us also.
NEZZEMUT: What an idea to have! What of Akhnaton?

NEFERTITI: [*turning her head*] Hush – see, there he sits. I am so frightened for him. He is ill.

NEZZEMUT: There, there, sister.

NEFERTITI: I am so glad you have come. [*Draws her down L.* PARA *follows them.*]

NEZZEMUT: Yes, yes.

NEFERTITI: I've been so frightened.

NEZZEMUT: Silly little thing.

NEFERTITI: I feel as though all my world was falling to pieces.

NEZZEMUT: I admit things aren't exactly cheerful.

NEFERTITI: [*lowering her voice*] But it's Akhnaton, really, I'm so frightened about! I'm sure he's very ill. He just sits there staring in front of him – he doesn't hear me when I speak to him . . . Oh, what shall I do?

NEZZEMUT: There, there. [*Turning to look at* PARA] I know what we will do. Para shall make one of her famous brews of herbs for him.

[*A look of significance passes between her and* PARA.]

You understand, Para?

PARA: Yes, mistress. [*Goes up to door.*]

NEZZEMUT: Use all your skill.

[PARA *goes out.*

NEZZEMUT *and* NEFERTITI *go on to couch and sit together.*]

NEFERTITI: [*stroking her sister's arm lovingly*] And you have

144

not deserted me – you have not deserted me. Dear sister. Dear Nezzemut.

NEZZEMUT: [*uncomfortable, trying to speak lightly*] For goodness' sake, don't let's be so tragic. Desert you indeed.

NEFERTITI: But why did you go away?

NEZZEMUT: Well, you know, my dear, here we all live with our heads in the air. I thought it was time someone with a little common sense found out exactly what was going on. You're all so unworldly.

NEFERTITI: You know Tutankhaton has gone to the City of No?

NEZZEMUT: Yes, the priests have got hold of him. You can't really blame him. Things are going to rack and ruin in Egypt. But it will be all right. Horemheb will pull things together.

NEFERTITI: [*bitterly*] Horemheb.

NEZZEMUT: [*sharply*] Has he been here?

NEFERTITI: Yes.

NEZZEMUT: [*more sharply and uneasily*] What did he say?

NEFERTITI: What should he say? The rat leaves the sinking ship.

NEZZEMUT: [*thoughtfully*] I see. [*Pause.*] He didn't say anything – particular.

NEFERTITI: He talked about Egypt.

NEZZEMUT: Of course. He would. Did he mention Tutankhaton or – or anyone else?

NEFERTITI: No.

[NEZZEMUT *breathes a sigh of relief.* PARA *enters with a gold cup.*]

PARA: Here is the draught, mistress.

[*She and* NEZZEMUT *exchange a glance of understanding.*]

NEZZEMUT: [*taking cup and handing it to* NEFERTITI] Para's a wonder. Her herb brews are simply too marvellous. You give Akhnaton this.

NEFERTITI: He won't take anything. He hasn't eaten or drunk since yesterday.

NEZZEMUT: Nonsense, you must make him. [*Rises.*] I'll leave you to it.

[*She goes up to the door, hesitates, then goes out.* PARA *follows her.*

NEFERTITI *carries cup to* AKHNATON.]

NEFERTITI: Dear lord.

[AKHNATON *does not answer. She sets down cup and strokes his sleeve then his hand.*]

Come back, dear lord, come back.

[AKHNATON'*s rigidity stirs.*]

It is Nefertiti – Nefertiti, the Royal Wife.

AKHNATON: [*dreamily*] The Royal Wife. [*With a sudden smile*] The Great Royal Wife.

NEFERTITI: [*delighted*] Yes. Listen, dear lord, you must not sit so long like this. You must eat and drink.

AKHNATON: [*from far away*] How shall I eat and drink when I bear all the sorrows of the world?

NEFERTITI: But to please me.

AKHNATON: [*with a touch of wildness again*] The Divine Aton has departed from me. I am alone.

NEFERTITI: [*bringing cup*] Drink, dear lord, drink from this cup that my hands hold for you.

AKHNATON: [*realizing her again*] Gentle hands – lovely hands – the beautiful hands of Nefertiti. The hands that put the Aton to rest.

NEFERTITI: Yes, yes. The hands that bring you rest and refreshment.

AKHNATON: [*taking cup from her*] From your hands to my lips. [*He drinks.*] A strange bitter draught. [*Gives back cup.*] I will not finish it.

NEFERTITI: It will do you good, my dear one. It will bring you strength and new life.

AKHNATON: New life? [*Musingly*] New life? Is this new life that creeps sluggishly through my veins – this creeping coldness – this dimming of a last fitful fire – [*His head drops forward.*]

NEFERTITI: [*a little anxiously*] It will make you sleep.

AKHNATON: The sun sinks below the horizon . . .

NEFERTITI: [*looking to window*] Not yet.

AKHNATON: [*heavily*] The sun sinks . . . You must take the jewelled sistrums – and put the Aton to rest in the temple ceremony.

NEFERTITI: Not tonight. Tonight I stay here with you.

AKHNATON: So cold – so cold – like an image of stone . . .

[*Enter* NEZZEMUT. NEFERTITI *tiptoes over to her.*]

NEFERTITI: I have made him drink it.

NEZZEMUT: [*with a sigh of relief*] Good.

NEFERTITI: He is very cold – he feels like stone. Will it make him sleep?

NEZZEMUT: Yes, yes, he will sleep, and tomorrow wake refreshed.

NEFERTITI: [*sighing*] That is well. [*Goes over and picks up cup.*] I, too, will sleep. [*Raises it to her lips.*]

NEZZEMUT: [*startled*] No, no, not you.

[*Runs across and tears it from her lips, but* NEFERTITI *retains her hold, staring at* NEZZEMUT *with dawning comprehension.*]

NEFERTITI: [*with full comprehension*] So that is it!

NEZZEMUT: [*frightened*] Nefertiti, I swear to you . . .

NEFERTITI: The swift and painless death of which Para knows the secret . . . The draught for which there is no antidote . . . And *my* hands gave it to the King . . .

NEZZEMUT: [*frantic*] It was a mistake – a mistake, I tell you!

NEFERTITI: [*scornfully*] A mistake.

NEZZEMUT: Yes, indeed – I only feared – [*Breaks off before* NEFERTITI's *scorn.*]

NEFERTITI: [*with anguish*] Oh, is there no truth anywhere? Is there nothing but betrayal?

NEZZEMUT: [*terrified*] Sister, have mercy – don't have me put to death.

NEFERTITI: [*with cold scorn*] In the City of Aton there is no putting to death. Death comes from the City of Amon. Return there to your master and tell him the plan went well . . .

[NEZZEMUT *creeps out.*

NEFERTITI *stands for a minute then goes slowly over to* AKHNATON *and falls on her knees beside him, weeping silently.*]

These accursed hands – accursed hands –

AKHNATON: [*from far away*] I cannot hear what you say.

NEFERTITI: My love, my lord – oh, your cold hands – like stone – [*Takes them.*]

AKHNATON: Let me see your face – I cannot move my body – it is heavy like stone. Only my head feels still alive.

NEFERTITI: Oh cruel – cruel.

AKHNATON: [*urgently*] Your face – I must see your face – the beautiful face of Nefertiti. Let it be the last thing I see.

[NEFERTITI *rises, dashes tears from her face, then seized by inspiration she takes from its place the modelled head of her and, carrying it, places it so that the last beam of the sun strikes it where* AKHNATON *can see it.*]

NEFERTITI: Can you see, dear lord? [*She stands in shadow.*]

AKHNATON: Ah! [*With deep satisfaction*] How beautiful. I never knew till now how beautiful you are, my Royal and beautiful wife.

[NEFERTITI *covers her face with her hands.* AKHNATON's *eyes slowly close. She comes back to his side as the beam fades from the bust. She drops down, her face in her hands.*]

[*Haltingly*] Dark . . . cold . . .

[NEFERTITI *sobs.* AY *enters in a state of alarm.*]

AY: [*in an agitated whisper*] What is happening? The Princess — she has left again —

NEFERTITI: Let her go. She has done her work.

AY: [*peering in gloom*] What work?

NEFERTITI: The work of Amon.

AY: I do not understand. [*Weakly*] I am growing old.

[NEFERTITI *comes across to him.*]

NEFERTITI: Listen to me, Ay. These are my commands the commands of the Queen, [*proudly*] the Great King's wife, his beloved, the Mistress of the Two Lands, Living and Flourishing, Nefertiti! [*Pause.*] Hear and obey. Let none enter this chamber till the Aton rises in the Heavens. Then let the King's body be conveyed to the tomb prepared for it.

AY: [*horrified*] The King —

NEFERTITI: [*cutting him short*] The King will not live till morning. Let all models made of my hands be taken out and broken with a hammer and utterly destroyed, for the hands of Nefertiti are henceforth accursed since they have brought Death to the lips of her lord. [*Pause.*] Let the portrait head of me that stands here and which was made by the hands of the King be buried secretly where no man knows. So it may be that it shall escape the destruction of the city which shall surely come at the hands of Amon. [*Dreamily*] And it may be that in far off years it shall be found and men shall say, 'He who made this was one of the greatest sculptors the world has ever known.' So, though the name of Akhnaton perish, the beauty he made shall still live. [*Pause.*] Listen to my last command, Ay. My body shall not be laid in its prepared tomb. Let it be buried humbly, like a woman of the people, for my name is accursed for ever since I have destroyed the Son of Ra. [*As* AY, *bewildered, seems to be about to speak*] Speak no word, but leave me and remember my words. Let it be done as I, Nefertiti, the Queen, have said.

[AY *goes slowly out, a broken old man, weeping and murmuring to himself.*

NEFERTITI *takes up the cup and holds it, looking thoughtfully into it. Then she goes to* AKHNATON *and touches his head and lays her hand on his heart, shakes her head, her meaning being he still lives. She crouches down beside him and places the cup near her. Several minutes pass. It is almost dark as the door bursts open and* HOREMHEB *staggers in.*]

NEFERTITI: Who dares to enter against my spoken command?

HOREMHEB: What have I done? What have I done?

NEFERTITI: Why have you come?

HOREMHEB: To have loved and to have destroyed? Can anything be greater sorrow?

NEFERTITI: I do not know.

HOREMHEB: It were best that I died here – by my master!

NEFERTITI: Not so. You have betrayed once. Do not

betray a second time. To live for a cause, not to die for it – that is your lot.

HOREMHEB: You did well to hate and fear me always.

NEFERTITI: I hate you no longer. [*Slowly*] We both loved him. Between us we destroyed him. There is no greater sorrow than to destroy that which you love.

HOREMHEB: Who has done this thing?

NEFERTITI: Does it matter?

HOREMHEB: [*with horrified conviction*] The guilt is mine.

NEFERTITI: [*impatiently*] Words – words! It is deeds that matter, remember, Horemheb! There is no room for you here. Egypt awaits you.

HOREMHEB: Egypt? Do I love Egypt as I love – him?

NEFERTITI: Go!

HOREMHEB: Akhnaton – Master. My dear, dear lord . . .

NEFERTITI: He cannot see you, nor hear you . . .

HOREMHEB: Akhnaton . . .

NEFERTITI: [*with force*] Go!

[*Their eyes meet. It is a duel.* HOREMHEB *is vanquished. He turns and stumbles out.*

NEFERTITI *touches* AKHNATON'S *hand, his head, crouching against him. Then she takes the cup in her hands. A faint tremor passes through* AKHNATON'S *body. She feels it and looks up. His eyes open. A shaft of silver light shines down on him.*]

AKHNATON: [*in a clear voice*] O my Father Aton, I breathe the sweet breath which comes from thy mouth. I behold thy beauty . . . I hear thy sweet voice, even the north wind. My limbs are rejuvenated through love of thee. Give me thy hands, holding thy spirit that I may receive and live by it. [*Pause.*] Call thou upon my name to all Eternity and it shall never fail . . . [*He dies.*]

[NEFERTITI *lifts cup to her lips as the curtain falls.*]

CURTAIN

EPILOGUE

CAPTAIN: In the name of the Great King, Mighty Bull, Ready in Plans, Creator of the Two Lands, King of Upper and Lower Egypt, Beloved of Amon, Horemheb. Amon King of Gods is the protector of his limbs. His Majesty has sailed down stream, he has organized this land. He has restored the temples. He has shaped their images once more, increasing their beauty. He has raised up new temples, he has fashioned a hundred images with all splendid costly stones. He furnished them as they had been in the beginning. He has established for them daily offerings. He has equipped them with priests. All the vessels of the temples are of silver and gold. He has given to them lands and cattle. Heaven is in festivity, Earth hath joy. May the Great King Horemheb and the Great Queen Nezzemut live in joy as the whole land rejoices.

[*The* PEASANTS *shout applause.*]

These are the commands of His Majesty; there shall be no oppression in the land. If any soldier is guilty of

extortion, or threats, his nose shall be cut off. If hides are
stolen the offender shall be beaten. Neither grain nor
vegetables shall be stolen. Dishonest tax-gatherers shall be
severely punished. Judges shall be appointed throughout
the Kingdom to see that justice is done without fear of
bribery or corruption. For His Majesty shall legislate for
Egypt to prosper the life of its inhabitants.

[*More sound of applause from* PEASANTS.]

Thus saith the divine Amon, King of the Gods: 'How
many are the possessions of him who knows and fears
me. Wise is he who serves Amon, favoured is he who
knows him, there is protection and gold for him who
follows Amon.' Now, therefore, throughout the land,
the name of the criminal Akhnaton shall be blotted out.
His name shall perish from the land in loathing and
horror. His images in stone shall be destroyed, his name
erased. So let this criminal be forgotten and let him
disappear from the memory of men . . .

[*A murmur of assent goes up from the* PEOPLE.

The CAPTAIN *marches his men out, the* PEOPLE *disperse more slowly –*

The MASONS *resume their work. The sun rises and
strikes with its beams the defaced stone-work.*]

FIRST MASON: [*shielding his eyes*] Oh!
SECOND MASON: What is it, mate?
FIRST MASON: I can't see. The light's so dazzling.
SECOND MASON: It's the reflection of the sun.

FIRST MASON: When the light's too strong you can't see what you're doing.

[*A pause.*]

Come on. This job's got to be done.

[*They shield their eyes and resume chipping.*]

CURTAIN